Praise for
THE HEART OF THE LABYRINTH

Once in a while, a book comes along that kindles the fire of our inner wisdom so profoundly, the words seem to leap off the page and go straight into our heart. If you read only one book this year, this is it.

Nicole Schwab shines a powerful bright light on the dark crevices of our soul, revealing that what we are most afraid of dissipates in the light of wisdom, and more powerful than fear is love.

She shows us how we can consciously choose a different future by changing the beliefs we hold about who and what we really are. Her voyage of discovery becomes an odyssey of inner revelation and transformation. In her eloquent and inspiring description of her healing path, she shows us our own.

Dean Ornish, M.D.
Founder & President, Preventive Medicine Research Institute
Clinical Professor of Medicine, University of California
Author of *The Spectrum*

This book is alchemical, confronting and illuminating. Read it and relish the journey.

Clare Dakin
Founder, TreeSisters

I can't put it down. This is just what I needed to read right now. A really important book and one that should be seen by many.

Lynne Franks
Author, entrepreneur and women's empowerment guru

The Heart of the Labyrinth

Nicole Schwab

Womancraft Publishing

All characters in this work are fictional.

The Heart of the Labyrinth

Cover Design: Design Deluxe

Published by Womancraft Publishing, 2014
www.lucentword.com

ISBN: 978-1-910559-00-0

The CO_2 emissions arising from the production of this book have been offset by the author. For more information see: nicoleschwab.com/books/offset

To Jay,

Who walks with us through the night

And holds the torch

Until we find

The source of our own fire.

Acknowledgments

My profound gratitude goes to Jay Schumacher, for taking me to the heart of the labyrinth, for the numerous conversations that sparked my imagination and prompted me to jump wholeheartedly into the luminous adventure of writing this book, and for his feedback and support that helped me gain ever-increasing clarity as I crafted this story.

My parents, Hilde and Klaus, who have always lovingly and unquestioningly supported my arcane adventures and explorations.

Rosmarie Bryner, who shared her grounded wisdom and generosity with me and offered me an earthen home in a magical place amidst olive trees that breathes of the Oracles of times past. Our four-legged friends who kept me company and gently nudged me into a playful enquiry with life.

Clare Dakin, my sister on the journey. Dan Emmons, who taught me how to experience the meeting of the dense and the subtle.

Viviana Gozzi, for adding depth and beauty to the world with her brushstrokes. Nancy Connelly who helped me smooth the edges, and Lucy Pearce, who enriched the final version of the story with her precious insights and suggestions.

And Life, my beloved Gaia, my other body, the greatest Teacher of all.

Publisher's Foreword

I first met Nicole Schwab online at a women's leadership teleconference. Womancraft Publishing had only launched a few days earlier.

She submitted her book within hours. And it instantly captivated me. It was reminiscent to me of the work of Paolo Coelho, Lynn V. Andrew's *Medicine Woman* series and *The Celestine Prophecy*. And yet it was also unique. Filled with exotic landscapes, powerful spiritual lessons, beautiful writing... this was the work of a woman of deep soul, profound understanding of the human condition, who spoke of the divine feminine in language which resonated with my own beliefs. This book had to be in print. And I was honored that it was being offered to Womancraft Publishing, as our first book.

Nicole's work is in the tradition of many spiritual teachings: using story or parable as a vehicle for transmitting profound truths direct to the soul. And in the tradition of many women's writings, she blurs the lines between traditional genres of fiction, non-fiction and poetry. She weaves stories within stories. Dreams, visions and different lifetimes, are blended in a rich satisfying narrative which nourishes the spirit and mind.

As I began editing the book, the themes and teachings became hugely relevant to my own life. I was struggling with constantly recurring bouts of ill health, and found myself traveling a similar journey to the book's protagonist, Maya. I found myself looking again at my own life, work, and inner workings, and found Nicole's teachings hugely prescient, and insightful and deeply helpful on a personal level. It was as though the book I most needed, had landed right in my lap. And I had the privilege of working on it, shaping and crafting it, shining its beautiful facets.

I humbly, but with deep enthusiasm, commend this book to you as a powerful companion on your journey. May it be the guide you need in your inner explorations. May it help you see yourself and your inner life with new eyes. May it develop your own ecological awareness, your connection to Source and the divine feminine, helping you to reclaim your spiritual nature embedded in this precious Earth that we inhabit.

Lucy H. Pearce, Cork, Ireland
Womancraft Publishing

About the Author

Nicole Schwab is an earth-loving, deep-thinking author and social entrepreneur who spent the last twenty years living and working across cultures and horizons, striving to create a harmonious sustainable world, one that values and honors the feminine principle, and is rooted in our connection to the Earth as a living being.

After a rigorous scientific training – degrees in Natural Sciences from Cambridge University and in Public Policy from Harvard Kennedy School – she moved to the Andes to work on maternal and child health programs across Latin America, becoming intimately acquainted with the indigenous culture of the highlands. Returning to her native Switzerland in 2004, she set up the Forum of Young Global Leaders at the World Economic Forum, and facilitated the nascent community's exchanges around a vision for the world in 2020.

In 2009, eager to intensify her engagement on behalf of the feminine, she co-founded The Gender Equality Project – now called EDGE Certified Foundation – a global scheme that certifies companies for closing the gender gap in the workplace. As the project matured into a phase of expansion, Nicole retreated to the mystical ruins of ancient Greece, to honor her lifelong calling as a writer and give voice to her deepest insights and experiences in her first book, *The Heart of the Labyrinth*.

nicoleschwab.com

I

Falling in

Maya

I was born on the winter solstice the year our people lost their land. I didn't know this until much later. I didn't know anything about my past until I started asking, digging the earth with my bare hands to uncover my roots. Until I embarked upon a journey to the deepest recesses of my mind and was led to places nobody would want to go, for fear of coming face to face with the darkness. But I did, and I found my way through to the other side.

They say I was born in the forest. They say that my first contact with the world was the touch of the soft earth, moist and raw. The touch of my earthen mother, who received me even before I sensed the touch, smell and face of my human mother. And she has never forsaken me. She has been with me every breath along the way. But I was blind to Her magnificent presence, gently guiding my steps through the labyrinth of life.

They say that a few days after I was born, my birth mother

brought me to the city, wrapped in a woven blanket. She brought me to that place in the night, where the shadows and the howling dogs cry the pain of separation, moved by the hopes and wishes for a better life that all mothers deposit along with their heart as they tear themselves away from their own flesh. And so she did.

I can see it clearly now: how she lifted the iron shutter that opened onto the inner courtyard of the little adobe house in the center of the city. On the other side was a broad windowsill, specially crafted for receiving newly arrived souls, the ones that couldn't be kept, the ones that were somehow not quite born in the right place, at the right time. She deposited the bundle and left without a trace in the pale shadow of a yellow moon.

Magdalena was sitting inside, smoking a cigarette, listening to the familiar sounds of the night, stray dogs fighting, faint honking and music in the distance, broken glass left behind by a stumbling drunkard. And then she heard the unmistakable sound. The rusty iron shutter sliding open, muffled sighs and the shutter sliding closed again. Her heart tightened as she felt the pain of the tear. She waited. There was no cry. The baby was probably asleep.

After a deep sigh, she walked over, hoping that perhaps it had been her imagination. But no, there it was: a carefully wrapped bundle. And inside, all she could see were eyes. Huge green eyes, wide open, staring up at the lights, looking into her eyes, questioning, questioning. A gaze so deep, so ancient, so knowing. She shuddered. It was as if those eyes were looking straight through her, daring her with the most profound of questions: Who am I? What am I? Why am I here?

That's what she told me, thirty years later, when I found her in her little house hugging the illegally built flanks of a landslide prone city. I was adopted shortly thereafter by my parents, the ones who live in the United States. But even though I was in her care for only a few weeks, she always remembered my eyes. The questions that formed in her mind upon meeting my gaze unlocked a door in the depth of her being that changed the course of her life. In her heart, she knew that she would see me again some day. But we will get to that later.

Let's start again at the beginning, the other beginning: I grew up in a small town on the north eastern coast of the United States of America. My father was a Protestant priest. He was a good man, but very stern and demanding, striving to model his life after that of Jesus. His air of severe righteousness spread to all those around him, with the silent expectation that they too follow the path of the sinless who will inherit the Kingdom of Heaven.

His sermons were well attended, but as I became older, I wondered whether anyone really understood what he was preaching. His analysis went deep, but it was highly intellectual and philosophical. Judging by the somnolent nods, faint giggles and whispers that sometimes echoed between the wooden benches, it seemed that most of the pious crowd came out of habit, rather than for a source of intellectual nourishment, let alone spiritual enlightenment.

The church was my second home, along with the forest, but I wasn't allowed to spend much time in what was considered 'the wild'. So I played in the gravel courtyard behind the church, not far from the graves, and climbed up and down the spiral wooden staircase, exploring the cobwebs and hidden corners of the bell tower. There was nothing inside the church, apart from a large wooden table with a big white candle and an old open bible that I wasn't allowed to touch. Right behind it, hung an imposing cross, threatening to fall down at any moment, an injunction to stay on the path. That was all.

What I liked most was to sit on one of the wooden benches, listening to the organ breathe its sublime sounds into the nave, whilst watching the beams of light play with the dust particles suspended in the bright colors of the stained-glass windows.

It was like an open gateway into another world. A world of beauty and color, a world of joy where life flowed with ease and laughter and all was possible. It was a world holding many forms of life, people, animals, and etheric beings, all surrendered to the infinite sense of being that was their very essence. It was a world where all was possible, all was allowed, and yet all was in perfect harmony for duality had been transcended.

These words come to me now to describe what at the time was a journey without words. All I had to do was come in when the sun was out, when the organist was playing, sit in a particular spot, focus my eyes on the shimmering dust and the gate would open. My being would dissolve into another reality more tangible than my daily life. It was a dream-world of adventures, conversations and friendships, but I was not dreaming. I was wide-awake.

I only tried to explain it once, when my father observed me sitting there in what he called a hypnotic stupor and asked me what I was doing. The more I tried to explain the gate to the dream-world and the beings there, the more he became agitated and I realized that some things are best not spoken of. It was perfectly normal for Ezekiel to have visions of strange winged creatures and speak with God, or for Jacob to fight with an angel, but it was not acceptable for the priest's daughter to have conversations with fairies and animals, for that surely was the product of an over-active imagination prone to temptation.

At times, I also found them as I ran in the fields, in the silver whispers of the streams, in the fine mist gently playing with the wind, or in the golden leaves falling silently upon the first winter snow. There were moments of magic in nature, on the rare occasions when I was playing outside on my own, when I would blink, and in that blink, enter into the other world. Everything was the same. Yet everything was different. Shining more brightly. All interconnected. I was the Earth and as I walked, I delicately set my feet upon myself. The trees and the stones were me. The squirrels running up the trees were also me. It was so wonderful and so funny. I could only marvel, roll around in the grass and giggle up to the great sky. Until a stern human voice called me home…

The years passed, and slowly, the reality I had been graced with in my childhood faded away. I spent less time in nature and more time in school. My mind decided that what I had experienced as real had only been an illusion, a play of my childish imagination. The voice inside me that told me I was different, that the blood of the Earth flowed in my veins, and that the forest was my home, was silenced. My skin was golden and my hair black as the night, but somehow, all the messages and influences around me reinforced the fact that I was just like everybody else, that my future would be determined solely by my education and my intelligence. And so, I studied hard, doing my best to earn my parents' love and approval.

The most important thing was to be a good Christian, and I wholeheartedly embraced the teachings. Most of the stories seemed oddly familiar and in their inner core spoke to a knowing that was alive somewhere within me, but that I couldn't quite access. Jesus was my friend, an ally and refuge. Even in my most rebellious teenage years, he was there, with his infinite love and kindness, forgiving all, embracing all. Even when I questioned the outer form – and question I did – there remained a grain of dust that contained everlasting truth.

But being a Christian also meant that as I grew up, the options before me were pretty slim: one could either become a good mother and wife, a virgin – who knows, one might even bear the son of God – or one could become a good working man. Since neither virgin, nor good mother and wife appealed to me, I opted for 'good working man'. I didn't do this consciously, of course, but in hindsight, it was my only choice. These were the tracks laid out for a whole generation, and for those like me whose highest internalized longing was to be a good little girl, breaking the rules to create new options was beyond the realm of the possible. And so, like many others, I followed the pack, all the while thinking I was free.

Year after year, the alienation continued, the impressions seeped in to my bones, staining my very essence. I was accepted by a good college, received what was considered an excellent education with awards and accolades, and then went on to a high-earning job, a brilliant career. Achievement was my only goal, the mark of success, proof that I had finally reached the 'good working man' status, which came with money and power. The fact that I was a woman did not seem relevant as long as I followed the spotlessly clean trail paved by the men who came before me, who had cleared the wilderness to erect the cathedrals of the modern world.

My life was entirely built on and in service to the most Holy of Holies: the intellect, freeing man from his abject savage condition. The wild had long been muzzled and subjugated, relegated to an obscure corner of my soul, from whence it only dared growl once in a while, in moments of weakness and loss of self-control, soon to be cornered and silenced again. Of course, I had emotions and I appreciated art, but it was all in an intellectual kind of way. The armor I had built to suppress feelings was so strong by then, that even when they broke through, they were quickly intellectualized and their sparks extinguished, lest they set fire to the whole crumbling edifice of the civilization I had grown up in.

What a glorious time it was. I had control over everything in my inner and outer life, and dedicated all my efforts and knowledge to keeping it so. Life was going faster and faster. There was always more to do, more projects to undertake, more trips to go on, more people to meet, more deals to make. It all made sense in this perfectly organized structure that I, just like all those around me, had so carefully built around myself. I worked for a big company because it was a good thing to do. I consumed because I believed that economic growth was the solution to the ills of under-development. And I lived my life as a good citizen, upholding fairness and justice.

In short, I blindly accepted the beliefs of my generation.

But then, one day… lightning struck.

In the high plains of the Andes, they say that if you are struck by a bolt of lightning, it is a sign. It is the mark of the shaman, the one who is blessed with fire and survives. The one who has befriended the Great Spirit and can henceforth serve as a bridge between the seen and the unseen.

It had been a particularly exhausting month. For years I had been working without taking more than a few days off. My body was showing signs of exhaustion, and I started suffering from recurring migraines, skin rashes and stomach aches. But my willpower was strong, my mind was sharp and I had convinced myself of my impermeability to such physical ailments. So I ignored whatever came up and plunged wholeheartedly into the tasks of the day ahead with all its demands and deadlines, overriding any discomfort.

My friends had started voicing concerns at my pale complexion and the dull look in my eyes. After years of convincing myself that I was not different, I had even managed to deprive myself of life to such an extent that my skin was ashen, with dark half-moons under my eyes – the subtle trace of the wise one I had banished from my life. I had just turned thirty and should have been in the prime of my vitality, but life was being sucked out of me with every passing day.

I knew this was happening. Of course I knew. But I pretended

I did not see. I pretended that I was still in control, that nothing would ever change. My life wasn't any different from the lives of my friends and colleagues. Why should it exhaust me more than them? Besides, I believed that I was indispensable to my company. After so many years of effort, I had reached a position of responsibility where my constant presence was necessary. Decisions had to be made, projects carried forward, reports conceived and written. Employees sought my advice and my boss expected me to deliver on my division's targets. I felt I had no choice but to continue on the track I had committed to.

What I didn't know at the time was that I am of those who have been given to the Earth at birth, who have been initiated in Her secrets in the early dawn of our lives. And for us, the price we pay when we stray from the path is, most often: our life. She was calling me, but I couldn't hear Her. She was speaking clearly, but I failed to understand.

I had just been on my last long business trip of the year. On the road back to the airport, I stared sadly out of the cab window at the thick man-made fog, dulling the sunlight I had so loved as a child. Until then I had been blind to the grayness of the skies, too busy to even notice. But for some reason, in that instant, I suddenly became fully aware of it. I was shocked to realize that the air pollution was so severe that cities were becoming uninhabitable for the very humans that had built them. And yet, those same humans continued their daily lives, obediently adjusting by wearing masks and staying indoors, like blind sheep ignoring the gas chambers they were slowly but surely building around themselves. I couldn't help but wonder what our collective future would bring.

Just like everyone else, I read the news and absorbed the terrible stories that were spoon-fed to us day after day, stories of famine and poverty, war and natural disasters. Until then, however, they had always seemed removed, far away from my daily troubles, as if I was living in a parallel universe. I had become used to absorbing world events whilst going on with my business, numb to the world around me. I had been making money and spending it, as if my actions were of no consequence in the face of the magnitude of the drama unfolding on the planet. Like so many others, I had convinced myself that being a good citizen participating in the prevailing economic system was the best thing I could do. This time, however, something had changed, there was a crack in the invisible layer of separation I had carefully constructed over all these years. The fog had seeped through into my body and soul, and I came home deeply disturbed.

Little did I know that my life would never be the same again. The morning after I landed, the alarm clock rang pulling me from the comatose depths of a dreamless world. I found that I was unable to move. I couldn't even open my eyes. Semi-conscious as I was, I didn't worry. I concluded it must be jetlag and gave up the struggle, allowing myself a few more hours of sleep.

When I woke again, the sunlight was coming in through the curtains. It was late. But again, I could not bring myself to a state of full wakefulness. My heart was pounding. My body was drenched in sweat. I felt dizzy and could barely move my limbs. But I had to go to work. They were expecting me. I just had to go. I forced myself up as best I could, mechanically got dressed and started searching for my car keys, only to come face to face with the reality that everything around me was a blur. I couldn't see properly; how could I drive? Powerless, I collapsed on my bed.

When I finally came to, I was still fully dressed, feeling terrible. I reached for the phone to tell my assistant that I was sick, adding that I would be in the office the next day. And then, darkness settled in. Several days passed like this. Every morning, I struggled to wake up and tried to force myself to get to work. But it just didn't happen. No amount of sleep seemed to satisfy my body. My mind was in a constant slumber. It felt as though a thick fog, much like the one I had witnessed on my trip, had descended upon me, playing a game that involved knocking me out completely or holding me in a semi-conscious drunken whirl. I felt increasingly guilty about the work that remained undone in my absence, attempting to ease my concerns by making elaborate plans in my head of how I would soon deal with it all.

Two weeks passed with no improvement, and I eventually gave up pretending that I would go back to work on the following day. I had called for help from my family and friends. But to my great shock and surprise, I soon found that I couldn't bear to have a conversation with anyone. The mental effort involved in listening to someone speak, let alone formulate a single sentence, required more energy than I had available. I couldn't interact with other humans, I couldn't sit in front of my computer, I couldn't read, and I couldn't even watch television. I had turned it on once, only to see trees being felled in a graphic documentary on deforestation. It was all too exhausting. The world had suddenly become too much. I understood that no matter how much I tried, I no longer had control over the state of my body. And in the brief moments when I truly surrendered, drifting in and out of a sleepless haze, I felt myself falling, falling deeply into another dimension within myself.

The days rolled on. Nothing changed. After a number of tests, the doctors concluded that all I needed was rest: a diagnosis that did not satisfy me in the slightest. By then, the professional commitments I had failed to honor loomed so large that the thought of having to face my boss without a valid excuse became unbearable. And thus, my mind stopped thinking about work and turned its attention to the dramatic condition of my body, sending all manner of fears to parade in front of my eyes. I had all the time in the world to entertain them, and they enjoyed the opportunity immensely, finally released from years of suppression. Perhaps my state would never change. Perhaps I had a rare, unrecognizable disease and life was drifting away from me. Perhaps I was dying.

What I didn't know at the time, was that my rapidly deteriorating state was a result of my single-minded obsession with work combined with the consequences of living in the world created by my generation and the one before us. Nor was I the only one suffering from what the medical establishment failed to recognize and refused to acknowledge. I had stretched my body so much, and for so long, that I had ultimately tipped it out of balance. And thus, overwhelmed and overburdened, my body was no longer able to deal with the increasing load of contaminants in my environment and simply acted as if everything around me had become toxic. Food was indigestible, water undrinkable and the air contaminated. The invisible electromagnetic smog emitted by the collection of devices in my apartment and the antennae surrounding me, burned my being and kept me awake night after night. After having slept through the initial weeks of my disease, rest suddenly became impossible, curtailing any chances of recovery.

The clouds were thickening and I was losing weight fast. Medical advice was sparse and useless at best, dramatic and depressing at worst. After another round of tests, the doctors concluded that I was suffering from a debilitating auto-immune disease. The prognosis was that I would never regain my health and that I would have to adjust my mind to the bleak realization that my life would henceforth entail living in an isolated environment. However, even this would not protect me from ongoing struggle and disease, and eventual premature death. Life as I had known it had come to an abrupt end.

I didn't know what to think of this prospect. For some reason, I couldn't bring myself to believe it. I desperately sought a solution by focusing on the question: where do I go now? If I can no longer live here, where can I live? I stayed in that state of darkness and struggle for survival for what seemed an eternity.

Every morning, as the sun stirred outside, I ignited hope and willed myself to get better, to recover the health I once had. I didn't understand that there was nothing to be recovered, for what was needed was the construction of an entirely distinct sense of healing and wellness, which involved much more than my physical body. Something different from what I had been taught was possible. In the depth of my despair, I called for help. I called out to the universe, to the God of my childhood, the elemental energies of nature, to all there is and all there might be. And then, one day, with the returning light of spring, a woman appeared at my door with words that would change my life.

I was lying in bed, alternating between moments of despair, and helpless surrender to the pain in my body when the doorbell rang. I hesitated. Facing another human along with the volatile toxins emanating from their breath, perfumes and clothing had become a risky affair that had the potential to send me plummeting into acute pain for days. The few friends and members of my family who brought me food and cared for me had all been warned and complied with strict instructions. I wondered who could be visiting me unannounced. The doorbell rang again with a persistence that suggested that whoever it was would stay there until I answered.

I got up, wrapped myself in a blanket and walked slowly down the hallway. "Who is it?" I asked, through the closed door.

A heavily accented woman's voice answered, "You don't remember me, but I know you. I have come a long way to find you. I have an important message for you."

My body instantly started shaking and sobs welled up from the depths of my being. With tears in my eyes, startled by my emotional reaction, I opened the door. I had given up trying to explain things logically and was ready to embrace any reality, no matter how strange it might seem, for the absurd and the insane could perhaps still offer me a few glimmers of hope.

Before me stood an old woman, her thick grey braids disappearing behind her shoulders. She wore feather earrings, a black dress and a beautiful embroidered purple shawl. Her dark skin seemed creased by lines of wisdom, and her eyes glistened like jewels, polished by the magma of life.

She smiled and opened her arms. Without thinking, I fell into the arms of this complete stranger, as in the arms of the Great Mother, sobbing uncontrollably. She held me for a long time, accompanying me into the apartment and onto the sofa. We sat there in silence and it seemed that much was being said beyond words. I was utterly confused. "You look so familiar. Who are you?" I asked.

"There will be time for that, dear Maya. For now, the only thing you need to know is that I have come from your past and I am here to help you." With that she lay her hand over my head and I slipped into a deep peaceful sleep, more restful than I had known for months, years perhaps.

As I opened my eyes again, the morning sun was sending rainbow-colored reflections across the room; it was a play of lights that echoed the mysterious words that had tumbled with me into wakefulness. Lingering words, hanging in mid-air, unwilling to leave, waiting for me to acknowledge their presence. I spoke them out, giving them the life they were beckoning: "You are not from here. You must return to the land of your ancestors. There, you will find healing."

And suddenly I remembered the previous night's visitor. There was nobody around, no sign of another human presence in my apartment, and the front door was locked. Yet, I realized that I felt better than I had for weeks, an unexpected flow of energy and life bubbling up in my body. Had I been dreaming? Where had she gone? How did she know my name? These words. What did they mean?

Before I had time to think this through, the phone rang. My mother. She said she was on her way and had something important to tell me. I knew something peculiar was happening. Perhaps I was losing my mind. But deep inside, something told me that I had never been more lucid, and that my call for help had been answered. I got dressed, prepared some tea, and waited.

She didn't bring me the usual home-baked muffins, which inevitably triggered her utter disappointment as I explained I couldn't eat them. This time, she had brought some apples from her orchard, a touching gesture to show me that she was doing her best to understand what my strange life had become. I didn't expect her to. I didn't expect anybody to grasp what was still an enigma to me. I knew how deeply she worried about my health, desperately hoping that her motherly love would cure me. But she never showed any of it, pretending that absolutely nothing had changed, that life was going on exactly as it always had. She still called me every Sunday asking why I hadn't come to church. She sometimes even asked how my work was doing and whether I had a business trip planned for the coming week. Her incapacity to acknowledge the truth of the situation deeply disturbed me.

She walked in and set the apples on the kitchen table. We sat down, facing each other in silence. She seemed agitated, afraid to look at me. When at last she spoke, she raised her eyes slowly and plunged them deep into mine, "Your father and I love you very dearly. We have done everything for you to grow up as a loved and successful woman. We never thought we would need to tell you this, but as you are so ill... perhaps it is best that you know." Her lips were trembling and I realized she was on the verge of breaking down.

"What is it?" I whispered, shivering, trying to conceal my fear. Perhaps she had called my doctor. Perhaps he had revealed to her that a new look at my last medical exams suggested an even shorter life expectancy than initially diagnosed. Perhaps she was going to tell me that I only had a few months left to live.

"We adopted you," came the answer.

I felt goose bumps all over my body. I recalled the previous night's visitor, the mysterious woman with feather earrings; her words, "You are not from here". She had not been a figment of my imagination after all. It was real.

And then my mother continued. An endless stream of words, all those words she had kept to herself for so many years in her desire to protect me from the truth. Teary-eyed she recounted the pregnancies she had, the miscarriages, the years of trying, until she and my father decided to adopt a child and flew to South America to find a lovely little baby with big green eyes who instantly became the treasure of their lives.

I sat there, at a loss for words. As I stared at the greying-blond woman opposite me, I suddenly couldn't believe that I had never doubted that I was her daughter. I was speechless.

She tried a smile, "And there is one more thing. Your name is the name your birth mother gave you. It was stitched on the blanket that you were wrapped in when they found you. We decided you should keep it as your heritage from your past. Here... I held on to this all these years."

She handed me a beautiful woolen blanket, woven in intricate earth-colored patterns over a deep red background, the four letters of my name sewn in a green silken thread across a corner. It seemed as if I was looking at the threads of my life crisscrossing the warmth of the earth. As I stared at them, a question formed, intense and urgent: Who am I?

My mother's words brought me back, "Regardless of what I just shared with you, you are and always will be our beloved daughter."

For a while, I sat there in silence, attempting a smile. It was so unexpected, so shocking. I was floating between worlds, wondering where I belonged. Would I find healing in the land of my ancestors, as the stranger had suggested? Without thinking, I looked at my mother and heard myself saying: "I need to go there. I cannot bear staying here any longer dragging myself through life day after day with no prospect of getting better. Perhaps this is a chance for me to find healing. Perhaps I might learn something important about myself."

She looked at me with sad, worried eyes. She didn't want me to travel. I was clearly not in a state to undertake a long journey, especially not to a place, which according to her, was ripe with strife and sparse comfort let alone any medical assistance should I need it. She assailed me with questions to make it unequivocal that my quest was unwise: Where would I go, once I arrived there? Who would take care of me? What if I didn't make it back? Besides, she had no information on my birth parents. She only had the name of the woman who had cared for me in the home for abandoned babies. What were the chances I would find her after so many years? She tried to dissuade me as best she could. I interrupted her. The discussion had exhausted me beyond what I could muster for the day and I asked her to leave so that I could rest and think about it.

That night, I had a dream. I was sitting on a mountainside overlooking a beautiful blue lake. The sun was shining intensely, warming my entire body. The wind was blowing gently, bringing to my ears the faint sound of a flute playing a melancholic tune. My hands were placed upon the ground, and little by little, starting at the fingertips, I became part of the earth, sinking in, disintegrating, and eventually disappearing completely. My body was no longer there, as if I had merged with something bigger and I was filled with a deep sense of peace. The flute kept playing and in its whisper I heard a woman's voice speaking to me. "Do not fear," she said, "you are coming back home."

It felt like an invitation, a guiding signpost on this new meandering path I had unwillingly stumbled upon. The journey seemed risky and the outcome uncertain, but my mind was made up. I would leave as soon as possible.

II

Achachilas:
Our Spiritual Ancestors

Saywa

My name is Saywa. I come from a family of pastors. We used to live close to the stars and follow the ways of our ancestors. I never learned to read or write. But I learned to decipher the soul and secrets of the life that breathes beneath the skies. I spent years sitting on the mountain, watching my flock of llamas. That was my task. And as I sat, I listened. There was much to learn from the whisper of the wind, the swaying of the leaves, the flight of a bird. My grandfather often sat with me and told me wonderful stories, stories of the Pachamama and her offspring, of the fire and lizards.

When we walked, we walked very slowly, and he would bend down every so often to show me a plant, and with a mischievous smile, he would embark upon another wild story, in which lay the keys to the plant's power and healing. He said they liked the stories. He said that telling them honored the spirit that resided within, and assured us their blessing. Through the stories, we were given permission to call upon their magic if we needed help.

Everyone in the family worked very hard. It was often cold and we all shared one small room in our adobe house. But there was always plenty of food and plenty of stories. And I loved sitting out on the mountain surrounded by my snowy giants. They watched over me. It was a wonderful time. I felt blessed.

Not long after I turned twelve, everything started changing, and it did so more rapidly than anyone would have predicted. The road had come to our village the previous year. Until then, we had been isolated from the outside world. Very few members of our community had ever left for the big city, and those who had seldom came back. We had only caught echoes of what life was like beyond our vast plains from the scant travelers who sometimes came through on mule-back, on their way to the great ancient ruins.

But with the road, the big city suddenly arrived at our doorstep. And with it, the golden promise of a life of ease and wealth lured more and more young people away from our ancestral ways. As I sat on my mountain, spinning wool and watching my flock, I started observing the cars driving in and out. I noticed a slight change in the melody of the wind, and was saddened to see the delicate vicuñas shy away to more remote pastures.

The village slowly emptied and life in the fields became harder and harder. There were fewer hands available for the patient communal labor of the earth that had yielded our food year after year. There were fewer hands available for the animals, the spinning, and the weaving. Our lives were becoming thinner and thinner in all dimensions, and the more they did, the more the city seemed the inevitable answer to our troubles.

One day, my oldest brother came back, driving a car, in fancy new clothes. He boasted of all the wonderful things he now possessed. He talked of a life of ease and freedom from the primitive ways of our ancestors. He talked as if it was madness for us to stay in this village that had been our home, breaking our backs day after day with such hard labor.

My grandfather took a deep breath and walked out the door. He never spoke again. I spent weeks begging him to tell me one more story, but in vain. He ignored my pleas, impassive, as if he had already left the world of humans and entered the muted state of our ancestors of stone, the Achachilas. He still sat with me on the mountain, but in silence. And one morning, as I turned towards his bed expecting it to be empty, I saw that he was still lying there. In that instant, I understood that he would never have left the village and that his soul had chosen to depart before giving us a chance to leave him there on his own.

I recalled his teachings on the cycles of life and death, on the turn of the wheel, which holds the universe in perfect harmony and constant evolution. I missed him deeply as I wandered out with my flock that morning, whilst my mother took care of preparing the three days of vigil. But I looked up at the mountains and consoled myself with the thought that he was watching over me from the eternal snows. I could almost hear his voice in the breeze, his laughter, his deep knowing silence.

Shortly thereafter, as expected, we too left the village. Life had become too arduous and with the coming of winter, the temptation to join my brothers in the city became stronger than the sweet whisper of the wind. We left the few animals we still had in the care of those who remained, packed our possessions and closed the door of our house. My heart tightened as the car drove away. I looked at my snowy giants. And I cried.

What lay ahead is a story I do not like to tell. It is a story of servitude and separation. When we arrived in the city, it quickly became clear that we would all need to work. I was given to a wealthy family as their servant. It was a common practice for girls my age. And so, I moved into a big mansion with shiny rooms. My task lay in keeping all of it clean, day after day, helping with the cooking and sometimes looking after the children who were not much younger than me.

I was fed simple but plentiful food and I had a tiny room all to myself, enough reason to be satisfied. Alas, my skin was darker than theirs, I was an illiterate indigenous girl, and this apparently gave them the right to treat me as a being of inferior rank. We lived in the same house, and yet, we moved in two separate worlds that they kept as far apart from each other as they possibly could. The other children played and went to school. I worked and was rarely allowed to leave the house. And on Sunday afternoons this difference in our inherent worth was driven home painfully: I had to prepare and serve the children their hot chocolate and cake. But I was never allowed to have any. So I retreated to the shadows of the kitchen door and watched them enjoy their treat, whilst resentfully sipping a cup of tasteless diluted tea.

I do not want to dwell on these years. More than anything, I suffered the separation from my world, from the gentle breath of life in the mountains. I no longer had time to be outside and my whole day was spent in tasks that felt futile and humiliating. The years passed and with them, I let go of the dreams of escape and return to the village I had harbored in the beginning. I worked and accepted my fate as if I was a puppet in the hands of strangers, with no power over my own life.

One day, death came knocking on the door. The old lady of the house passed away. She had been severe, but she had protected me from the whims of the ruthless male members of her family. Despite everything, I felt affection for her. I knew that it was her powerful matriarchal presence that had held in a temporary truce her quarrelling offspring. And with her death, as with the death of my grandfather many years earlier, change was in the air.

Once again, my world was shaken. I had strong reasons to fear for my safety and thus decided to leave as quickly as possible. I didn't know where to go. I had cut all ties to my family a long time ago and had barely left the mansion all these years. But the menace I felt from the men in the house was increasing by the hour. There was no time to waste. On the third night of vigil, whilst the extended family members were still sitting around the open coffin, drinking coffee and smoking cigarettes, I packed my bundle and slipped out, setting off in the dark towards the market at the other extremity of the city. It was the only place I was familiar with, and I knew that many women there spoke my language, their childhoods having been similar to mine.

I walked for several hours until I reached the small cobbled streets that weaved their way to the top of the city, through an endless maze of colorful stalls selling everything from fresh meat and vegetables, to clothing and plastic utensils. I went to find the lady who sold oranges, a big woman who always greeted me with a kind word and mischievous smile, proudly exhibiting her sparkling golden front tooth. She saw me coming from afar. It was still very early and all was quiet. She invited me to sit down on a piece of cardboard by her side, behind piles of oranges, and handed me a cup of freshly squeezed juice. She started chatting about her week, about the weather and the lives of the ladies who came to buy her fruit. I sat and listened, happy to have some company, not really paying attention to her voracious stream of comments.

And then, a word caught my attention, "...abandoned, so many of them. They can't feed them anymore, so they bring them to that place, hoping they will have a better life. And who knows, some of them probably do. These nuns are saints. Good women they are. So many children. Ay. They have more they can handle. Not many women know about the injections. In the villages they don't know. Or maybe they know, but they are afraid of their husbands. I was afraid too. But no one needs to know, I tell you. Five children! Ay. So much work…"

She paused to serve a customer. And before she was able to start again I asked her,

"Where is that place?"

"What place?"

"The house where they take care of abandoned babies."

"Oh, not far from here, just behind the meat section, below the little white church. If you stay a bit longer, one of the nuns will surely pass by and you can ask her. Why do you want to know?"

I sighed, "I… I don't know where to go."

"But you're not a baby!"

She roared with peals of laughter which echoed down the street. The neighboring vendors who had been listening to our conversation joined in heartily. I smiled. I could see the humor of the situation, even though they were laughing at my expense.

"Anyways," she retorted as she regained her breath, "they always need help down there, especially from someone like you who knows how to handle little ones. Not many people want to work there. It's too hard they say, to see them come and go like that. Maybe they'll take you. It's worth a try."

And so I waited, until, as the woman had said, a nun came by. And my life changed yet again.

The nuns gave me a new name, a Christian name. They called me Magdalena. And with that new name, I was reborn into a different life, which I loved. I lived in the house, helping the nuns take care of the babies and spent most nights under the crisp stars in the courtyard, ready to welcome new arrivals, should there be any. It was my favorite task. It was heart-breaking to imagine mothers separating from their babies, but I knew how hard life could be. Sometimes, one just needed to be given the opportunity to start again. And that's what we did: we gave them another chance.

The years passed and I worked with love and dedication. I took the babies in and cared for them as if they were my own. I loved them deeply, each and every one of them, learning the harsh lesson of unconditional love. No matter how much I wanted to keep them, I had to wish for them to leave and find a good home. I recalled the stories of my grandfather and spent hours telling them the tales of our ancestors, singing the melodies through which I had absorbed the deep wisdom of the Pachamama, our Mother Earth. It calmed them down, as if my voice and my words connected them back to the all-knowing source of life from which they had only recently been parted.

With the passing of time, I felt deeper and deeper levels of love well up from within. Just as I had cared for a flock of llamas when I was a little girl, I now had a flock of babies desperately calling out for warmth and affection. They cried a lot, some refused their food for days, even weeks. Some became very ill. And sometimes, tragically, we lost one. But we did the best we could with the meager means at our disposal, firmly anchored in our inexhaustible capacity to love.

I thought that I would spend the rest of my days there, that I had found my home and calling, that I would never feel the need to once again leave everything I knew and start afresh. But as I have come to know, nothing is permanent, and my life was shaken up again, not by death knocking at the door, but by the intense stare of a newborn life.

One night, like so many others, I heard the gate sliding open. I waited. And then, holding my breath, I stepped towards the entrance to see whether I would find a baby there. And find a baby I did. What a baby! She was wide awake, but she was not crying. She was looking up at the stars, and as I picked her up, her gaze met mine. Intense and profound. Emerald green, the color of the deep dark forests of the people who live beneath the clouds. As I stared into these eyes, I was struck by lightning, hypnotized, gazing through two open windows into the vast universe of my own soul.

I dissolved in their green mystery, and the floodgates of my memory were flung wide open. It was as if I had tapped into a part of myself, which lay outside of what I thought was 'me', and which I had never paid attention to. By acknowledging its existence, I brought it back to life, and in turn, it rewarded me with intense knowledge.

Time expanded, and I started catching glimpses of a distant past, faint memories of who I once was, who I really am. I suddenly recognized the little soul that I was holding in my arms and knew that our lives had forever been entangled. I wondered what paths we had walked, and shuddered as I instinctively grasped the profundity in our coming together once again.

III

Into the Cave

Maya

Suddenly the clouds parted and there it was: the city of the fallen stars. It was magnificent. The vast plains of the highlands abruptly ended below us, falling into a circular earthen bowl that had become the depository of myriad lights, mirroring the stars above, so close. I was breathless. All around, in the dusk, one could make out the bluish silhouettes of the giant mountains, stretching their snowy peaks through the clouds.

I had no idea what was going to happen next, how I would manage in this foreign place in the physical state I was in. "Maya, please come back as soon as possible," my mother had pleaded, as I announced my firm decision to undertake the journey. I didn't regret my decision, but the truth was I was afraid. The fever was sending chills through my whole weakened system. As I silently prayed that I would find healing, the man sitting in the aisle next to me leaned over and said, in broken English, "Don't be afraid. Everyone who comes here finds magic. It is very strong here."

And with that, the plane touched the ground and I was suddenly washed over by a strange wave of peace. I was home.

A few days later, having mustered enough energy to venture out of my hotel, I found myself standing in front of a small adobe house on the outskirts of the city. I had walked the dusty street up and down several times, followed by a couple of stray dogs temporarily abandoning their pile of garbage to try their luck with me. I had read the names on each entrance, again and again, almost ready to give up, when I noticed a rusty side gate, hidden in the shadows. There, I found the name I was looking for. My mother had given it to me before I left and the hotel manager had helped me find what seemed a possible address. I felt nervous as I stood there, catching my breath, not knowing what to expect. But the path had led me this far. It was too late to turn back. I rang the doorbell.

I heard shuffling sounds inside; a dog barking. The door creaked open and a young lady peered at me inquisitively. "I am looking for Magdalena," I said. Without a word, she invited me to step inside and led me down a corridor into a cozy little room, sparsely furnished, with big windows drinking in the translucent sunlight.

An old woman was sitting in a faded armchair by the window. She jumped out of her chair and came to greet me with open arms and a luminous smile, "Maya. I was waiting for you. It is so good to see you again!" she laughed joyfully.

There she was in her grey braids and feather earrings, her purple shawl pinned together over her long black dress with a beautiful silver brooch. I could barely believe my eyes. I was deeply moved by her presence exuding infinite love and compassion. Her amber eyes seemed to be laying their timeless wisdom onto the shores of my soul. My shivering body instantly relaxed; I forgot all my questions and fears. I felt as if I had arrived home after the exhausting journey of lifetimes. Utterly relieved, I let myself fall into her embrace.

"I am so happy you came, " she said. "In three days we will go to the island. It is a place of deep healing, from which no one returns unchanged. But for now, you must rest." She handed me a warm cup of herbal tea, explaining it was made of medicinal herbs she had picked for me that morning. She gently led me down the hallway to a tiny windowless room, just big enough to fit a bed. It felt like a cave, warm and safe, welcoming me back into the womb of the Great Mother.

We drove for several hours under the formidable spell of the chain of snow-capped mountains, stretching their peaks into the sky as they bore witness to countless cycles of human birth and death. We soon arrived at the shores of the majestic highland lake. They say that a whole civilization lies in its depths, the secrets of which are still available to those who have eyes to see. I instantly recognized the deep blue waters I had seen in my dream, the night I resolved to journey back to the land of my ancestors. The man on the plane had been right: there was magic in the air.

Magdalena shared stories from her life in the high plains and anecdotes about the places we were driving past. She paused for a while, and then, turning to me, she said, "I would like to sing you a song passed down to me by my grandfather. It is a song about our wonderful connection to the Pachamama, our Mother Earth. It is a song about a woman who honored her with every breath, with every gentle step. Because of her deep connection to the very source of life, she experienced daily miracles. All her questions were always answered from within. She had no doubts and no concerns, for the Pachamama took care of her wherever she went." After a pause, she added, "It is a song for you. In fact, it is a song about you. It may be too soon for you to understand. You may have forgotten, but now that you are here, it will all come back."

She started singing a wonderful tune in her language. I found her dedication somewhat confusing. A song about me? I wondered what it would be like to experience a profound connection with life, with the Earth, with each other. It was hard to even imagine. I had been raised to denigrate anything that was not of the intellect, to dismiss any alleged source of knowledge that lay beyond reason and analysis. Had I missed an essential part of what it meant to be human? A painful longing started to well up within me, and I suddenly felt immense grief for the loss of something I couldn't fully grasp yet, a loss I seemed to have unknowingly inflicted upon myself.

Magdalena stopped singing and we stayed in silence for a while as my tears slowly found their way through space back to the Earth. She took my hand and said, "Yes, Maya, you lost your Mother in the deepest sense. Not only were you separated from your birth mother who loved you so dearly. But you were torn away from the Pachamama, from that within you which knows. The world you grew up in taught you to suppress Her until you could no longer hear Her voice. This is why you are in so much pain. A pain that your body has been holding for years, begging you to listen. To listen and to remember that She is still here, waiting for you to notice Her again."

We had arrived at the shore of the lake. We boarded a wooden boat with a tiny puttering motor, which took us slowly over the still waters towards the island. Throughout the journey, Magdalena sang in a low voice, as if in prayer, her amber eyes lovingly taking in the horizon. As we arrived, she helped me out of the boat, smiled encouragingly and said we would need to walk the rest of the way. I felt very weak, but the intense sunlight, the crisp air and Magdalena's amazing presence gave me the courage to continue. I didn't know where she was leading me and did my best to keep up as she effortlessly climbed up the steep brown hill before us.

As if reading my mind, she turned and said, "We are going to see the Sage. For you to get better, you need to remember who you are. I can teach you to reconnect to the deep wisdom of the Pachamama; I can teach you to listen through your body, to dance and feel the inner truth alive within you. But because of the world you were brought up in, you also need to understand how your mind works. That's what the Sage can help you with: untying the knots and untangling the mess inside." She laughed, adding another of her mysterious comments, "He will be very pleased to see you again."

The view from the hilltop was breathtaking: we were at the highest point of the island, surrounded by the deep blue waters and the majestic backdrop of the mountains melting into the mist of distant shores. I noticed that the top of the hill was completely flat, as if its peak had been sliced away with a giant knife. In the center of this flattened area was a perfect circle of large white stones, equidistant to one another. It was a very beautiful, very peculiar place indeed.

"Legend has it that our divine ancestors sprang out of these waters at the origin of creation. They came out in the middle of the lake exactly where this island is now located. Step gracefully and perhaps you will feel their presence. They are still around."

I jumped. I hadn't seen him. An old man with fiery eyes and a pointy grey beard was sitting on a flattened white rock under a tree, outside the central circle. He didn't look like anyone else I had seen since I arrived in this country, or anywhere else for that matter. Something stirred deep inside of me. He gently looked at me, and I felt seen like never before, as if he was embracing the totality of who I was yet to become.

Magdalena and the Sage embraced, and he motioned us to follow him. On the southern side of the hill, a small footpath meandered its way down through some trees into another flattened grass-covered area, nestled against the hillside, protected from the winds. There was a central fire pit overlooking the lake. The narrow footpath continued on the other side of the opening, cutting across the hillside, and we soon found ourselves walking at the base of massive slabs of rock coming down vertically from the top of the hill.

After a few minutes of walking along in silence, he stopped and said, pointing towards the rock, "This will be your home now. Get some rest and meet us at the fireplace at sunset." And with a smile, they both turned and went back up the path, leaving me on my own in front of what looked like a cave. A cave! They must be joking. I was so shocked that I didn't move for a long time, and when I finally did, it was much too late to try to run after them. A cave! I was disgusted. I came from the other side of the world, severely ill, putting my full trust in these complete strangers, and the best they could muster was to give me a cave to sleep in. It was unbelievable.

The emotions started raging through my system. I alternated between fierce anger, and total depression, and eventually collapsed on the ground, leaning against the rock, right next to the entrance. The rock was warm from the afternoon sun, and it felt good on my back. My whole body was soaked in sweat, trembling from the effort and the emotions. I cried and curled myself into a ball, on the bare ground, now and then squinting through wet eyelashes to take in the vastness of the infinite blue horizon. Why had I come here?

Suddenly crisp and clear, I heard an answer, gentle and warm, "You are safer here than anywhere else. I will take care of you. I will show you the way back to full health and freedom, a life that you have never known could be possible. I will take you to the heart of the labyrinth and back out again a different woman."

I sighed. Not only was I in the company of complete lunatics, but I was also going crazy, hearing voices in my head, curled up like a wolf at the entrance of a cave. I had to laugh. It was all so ridiculously extreme. As I laughed, I felt the tension leave my body. And I heard the voice again, "You can come in now."

I turned towards the entrance. I had been too terrified to even look inside. I put my head through the narrow opening. On either side of the cave, three white candles were burning, and three more in the middle. I marveled as my eyes slowly got accustomed to the candlelit darkness. Once through the opening, I could stand again. The cave was of beautiful proportions, almost forming a perfect rocky dome. In the middle was what looked like an altar, with small rocks and flowers arranged around the candles on a black and red woven cloth. On the left side, there was a beautiful earthen bed, complete with mattress and wool blankets, and on the right, a number of alcoves had been sculpted into the rock forming natural shelves for various objects: books, jars, small statues. There were carpets on the rocky floor and contrary to my expectations it was neither cold nor damp inside. The air was fresh and the more my eyes got used to the darkness, the more I seemed to perceive a glow permeating the whole interior of the cave; a glow that did not come from the candles, as if the whole cavity was filled with barely perceptible golden particles.

It was so beautiful. All my fear and anger vanished and I felt ashamed at my earlier reaction. I listened intensely, but no voice was to be heard. So I lay down on the bed, my mind still on alert sending me images of the terrible spiders and snakes that must be swarming around, but I was too tired to heed them. As I closed my eyes, I caught a glimpse of a spiral pathway leading me straight down into the earth, but before I was able to ponder what that meant, I slipped into a deep sleep.

IV

Gaia's Prophecy

Saywa

It all started the night after I found Maya. What had been mere glimpses of another time and place, suddenly became fully fledged visions. For the first time I effortlessly slipped into a distant past and remembered it all.

I had been there at the beginning. I had suffered the first blow that would lead to the demise of the One who Knows. The end of an era. I had even known before it would happen. And I had told them. That was my role. That is what they had trained me for. To hear the voice of Gaia, our Mother, and speak it out for all to partake in the great secrets that only we had been taught to receive directly.

It all started on a winter day. There was frost that morning, and we went out early to play in the olive grove. Mother called. She asked us to comb our hair and said we would be allowed to go to the shrine and we must dress in white. The sun was rising, sending its golden warmth through the chill winter air. We gathered at the entrance of the sanctuary. The whole village was there, along with people I had never seen before. They looked like they had come from far away.

I was so excited. I had been waiting for this moment for a long time. As I climbed up the stone steps, holding my mother's hand, I felt transported. It was beautiful. Ochre cliffs formed a protective semi-circle behind us and before us, an emerald sea of trees wound their way down through the folds of the hills towards the blue waters. As we approached the sacred rock, together with a dozen other mothers and young girls from the village, my whole body started to shake. I felt as if I was being filled with bright light and started expanding, growing out of my body. And then the tears came. I didn't know why I was crying and why my body was shaking. I just remember thinking: I am going home.

The Priestess was looking at me. She came and took my hand and led me to the great rock, the one that had been split in two, from whence the vapors were rising. She asked me to put my hands on it, on either side of the clean cut. Her presence was loving and delicate and I did as she instructed. As I placed my hands on the warm stone, the feeling intensified. I could no longer feel my body. And as I looked up at the crowd standing in a semi-circle around us, I only saw light. Light everywhere, permeating everything in different shades. I felt I was going to faint, and that is when I heard Her for the very first time. Words formed in my mind, "Don't be afraid. You are now entrusted to my care and I will protect you for the rest of time."

As I opened my eyes again, I saw that the Priestess was holding me in her arms. We were sitting on the platform near the sacred shrine. She simply nodded, as if she knew, as if she too had heard the words, as if she too only saw light as her sparkling eyes smiled out at the men and women who were reverently staring at us.

It all happened very quickly. From that moment onwards, my life was devoted to Gaia, the Earth Goddess. I still lived at home, but I was entrusted to the old Priestess. Every morning, I completed the care-taking tasks she gave me and in the afternoons, she taught me patiently and lovingly, about Life, about the One who had showered us with Her grace. I learned about the skies and the sun, the moon and the sea. I learned about the plants that lived in the sanctuary, and I learned about grace and about healing.

She led me to the sacred rock once a week, so that I would learn to maintain a permanent connection with the source of Life. She taught me how to strengthen my body and purify my mind in preparation for channeling, through fasting and various breathing exercises. And every time I sat there, my body shook and my being expanded as the tears rolled down my cheeks. I never tired of marveling at the vivid colors and textures that suddenly pulsated all around me. Little by little, that state remained with me for prolonged periods, until I forgot what it was like to see, hear and feel in the way most humans did. I could no longer imagine living any other way. The time before had vanished.

Every day people came to honor Her. They came with gratitude in their hearts and blessings for the source of all Life. They brought offerings from the harvests, and the shepherds brought small sculptures of bone, wood and stone, crafted with devotion. Some also came with questions for the Oracle, seeking answers to bring their hearts peace and harmony. These were answered once a month, the night of the new moon. The role of the Priestess was to voice the answers that were given to her from the heart of the Earth. And I was to sit nearby and feel all that was occurring within and around me, until the day when it would be my turn to become the Oracle.

When I turned twelve, the old Priestess left her body. She came to me that evening and simply said, 'The time has come.' She lay down on the bare earth, on one of the level platforms behind the shrine, and peacefully closed her eyes. I covered her body with flowers and plants, as I had been trained to do, lit the oil lamps placed around her, and left. As I returned at dawn, she was no longer there. All that was left was her white robe and a beautiful rainbow-colored light, emanating from the earthen bed that had served as the sacred door to the other side.

I was not afraid, for She was there and I could turn to Her whenever I needed support or company, whenever I required guidance.

It was now my turn to conduct the blessings, and perform the rituals that gave rhythm to our lives, season after season. I was always intrigued when someone came from afar. From the sanctuary, we were protected by the mountains and could not see the blue bay below. When I felt them coming, I would climb high above the rocky cliffs and look out to see if I could spot a boat on the horizon. Usually, I did. As they came closer, I imagined them setting anchor, disembarking upon the firm land and starting the long pilgrimage through the olive grove that would lead them to the base of our sacred shrine.

Many years passed and eventually, I no longer needed to climb the mountain. I could simply close my eyes, and see all I wished to see, my being deeply anchored in the presence of Gaia. I was always ready the moment they arrived. They were welcomed and guided to an area by the stream where they could rest and prepare for the ceremonies.

I knew their questions before they even set foot in the sanctuary, but the answers were always withheld from me until the very last moment, for it was not for me to provide them. My role was to offer myself as a channel and speak the wisdom as it came, discovering the words upon my lips at the same time as the visitors for whom they were destined.

One day, after many years of devotion, I felt a great shadow descend upon the peaceful vibration of our land. Everything looked as usual. The sun was offering its beautiful late summer glow, the olive trees were bearing fruit and the birds were chirping joyfully. But something inside me was amiss. I felt called to receive Her words and embarked upon seven days of fasting and ritual ablutions. The other women caring for the sanctuary observed me with curiosity as there were no visitors and this was an unusual time to be preparing for such a ceremony. On the seventh day, I heard Her calling me. I went to the rock and sat in the anointed spot, feeling the light breeze caress my face and cover it every so often with a wisp of smoke coming up through the cracks, from the crystal heart at the center of the Earth. And then, the vision started. The shaking was stronger than usual. Tears flooded my cheeks. I physically felt an umbilical cord of light connecting me with Gaia. Her body became my body. Slowly, with great effort, the words formed, and I spoke.

"I have been your guardian and guide for millennia, holding you in harmony and peace, protecting you as you were protecting me, blessing you with abundance as you were blessing me with love and gratitude. This symbiotic relationship is soon going to end. Ahead of us lies a time of great turmoil. A time when humans will separate themselves from my body and no longer live in harmony but behave as a virulent parasite attacking its loving host. The disconnection will occur very slowly, over millennia, accelerating with the passing of time, as the memory of past rituals and grace fall into oblivion. Not all will be affected. Some women and some men will continue to feel Life pulsating through their veins. They will feel the pain of a dying tree in their own bodies, and cry in bliss at the sight of dew upon a newborn leaf. They will strive to restore harmony. But their struggle will be arduous and the outcome is uncertain.

"You will see the first changes in your lifetime. Very soon, boats with dark sails will appear on the horizon. A new ritual is set to replace what you have known here. Forceful control will slowly vanquish the gentleness and loving flow of your touch. The men of a warring God will slay the protective Spirit that has been guarding our shrine since the beginning of time. They will erect His temple upon my womb, and conquer the voice of wisdom for His own glory. The circle will be opened and straight lines will come to prevail, extending towards the skies in a futile search for what has been here all along.

"You and those who come after you will continue to be my Priestesses, and devote your lives to the sanctity of our relationship so that you may speak by me. The fame of your words will extend afar and more and more people will come from beyond the horizons to hear you, my Oracle. But with the growing stream of offerings, outer wealth will start shining in the eyes of men, and lure their actions away from life towards ever more riches. This will be the beginning of a time of decline. A time when your words will be interpreted through the filters of limited minds. A time when freedom of spirit is squashed under the weight of guilt and desire. A time when the feminine force of creation is enslaved and belittled for fear of its tremendous power.

"Millennia from now, upon the glorious ruins of the new temple, the Oracle will become a metaphor for the aimless wandering of countless disconnected souls in search for answers to their existential anguish. They will live outside of themselves and search in the external world for that which lies within the folds of the Earth, within the shimmers of their bleeding hearts.

"I offer two words, two drops of light to guide the ones who truly seek. These words will be engraved above the marble columns of the new temple, for all to remember. Once spoken, they will survive the march of the centuries, and illumine the darkness when the fire has almost been extinguished: *Know Thyself.*"

I collapsed and stayed in a semi-conscious state for several weeks after the last revelations. Not only had I received the words to be spoken, but I had seen before my eyes the images of the centuries to come, and they remained engraved in my memory. I was deeply saddened, yet also understood that this was part of the spiral process of evolution in which I had come to play a part.

No sooner had I recovered than I felt them coming. There were many boats. More than we had ever seen before. Their sails were dark red, the color of an earth of distant shores. As they walked up to the village, through the trees, I could sense the agitation of our villagers. The last words from the Oracle had echoed through the hills, repeated by many lips, undoubtedly transformed as they merged with each soul's hopes and fears.

But I was not afraid. I continued my devotional work and prepared for their arrival in the usual manner. I felt blessed to be able to partake in the process of spiritual evolution, be it for one more day, one more breath. I lived deeply anchored in Her, merged with the everlasting flow of Life permeating all things.

The first man who appeared at the precinct had the touch of the Gods. He was glowing with beauty and strength, fierce and gentle at once. I had never laid eyes upon such a man before, and wondered where he came from. He bowed deeply before me as was customary and handed me an offering for the great Goddess. A dark red silken cloth, lined with silver threads, delicately wrapped around a small statue of pure gold. We had never seen such riches and I was momentarily shaken by the beauty in my hands and that before me. I thanked him without words and walked slowly towards the altar by the rock to deposit the offering, bathing it in the glow of the shrine's fire.

The men and women who had come were kind and strong, and the villagers quickly forgot their apprehensions and fell under their spell. Aside from the offerings, they had brought quantity of foods and spices that we had never tasted, accustomed as we were to our frugal pastoral lifestyle. All were enchanted and we gathered to welcome them, just above the shrine, in the clearing reserved for important assemblies. The man who had brought the precious offering spoke. He celebrated the expanding fame of the Oracle, and the desire of more and more people to come and experience for themselves the grace bestowed upon those who entered the grounds of the sanctuary. He explained that they had been sent to build a temple in honor of their God, and that this was the chosen site, lying as it did at the navel of the world. He asserted that the temple did not seek to supplant the Goddess but rather to honor Her, and that the flow of people and fame it would bring would elevate the life of our villagers to a new prosperity.

I listened, seated on the side, close to the shrine. There was no doubt anymore: Her prophecy was to be fulfilled. His words signaled the first step into the future She had shown me; a future I would not have chosen. Yet, I had devoted my life to Her and would continue as long as she bade me to do so. After a silence, the man who was their leader turned to me. He bowed deeply and looked at me intensely, "Honorable Priestess, will our request receive a favorable answer?"

I lowered my eyes and said, "We will ask the Oracle."

She had already given us the answer, but they had to hear it directly from Her, so that the decision would lie in harmony with the flow of life. And I added, "We will meet again on the eve of the new moon, in front of the shrine. Prepare yourselves to receive Her grace in purity of heart and spirit."

I will always remember that night. I had been fasting for over a week and was in such a deep state that I did not pay much attention to all those who had gathered by the shrine. I never did, focusing entirely on my connection with Her. But as I walked slowly towards the dedicated spot, I noticed that there was one in the assembly whose vibration matched mine. It was him, of course. It felt as if he was holding the vibration with me, entering with me into the trance that opened the channel to the Source of Life. I had never experienced this before. Of course, the Priestess who had been my teacher had also held the vibration, but she had never merged her attention with mine, never focused all her power of awareness and connection on me. I was experiencing complete fusion with another human life in the most profound love and deepest bliss. As I sat down, a single word formed upon my lips. "Yes. The answer is yes."

Construction soon started. What had been a small precinct of plants and rocks, trees and flowers, was to become a temple complex of grandiose proportions, with giant columns erected towards the sky and a sinuous access pathway lined with stone slabs. Over time, a number of smaller temples would be added along with a giant amphitheater at the site where our assemblies were once held on the grass beneath the trees.

She had given me the instruction to choose and train the next Priestess. I was young still, but that message clearly signaled that my time in Her service was soon to come to an end. And so, as was customary, I took a young girl from the village under my care, to initiate her in all the secrets that my teacher had once shared with me.

Because of the constructions, we had suspended the ceremonies, and I no longer sat by the vapors to deliver the truth for others to hear. I still felt Her alive in my body, but I missed the intensity that took hold of me when speaking as Her Oracle. I wandered through the grounds, feeling nostalgic for the times before. And that's when life offered me another key to behold its mystery.

He came to me one night beneath the stars. I was sitting in

meditation, overlooking the valley, leaning against the rocky cliffs at the back of the sanctuary. I knew he was coming. I could sense his presence from afar. And he knew that I knew. My heart started beating faster, and my body was shaking. I felt the same intensity of connection as when I opened my being to Her. But this time, I was opening it to a mortal man, and yet, through him flowed a divine power that touched my heart deeply and elevated my whole being, expanding it into oceans of light. I felt his absolute devotion for the feminine fire that flowed through my veins, and I responded with the depth of my love, fully receiving his powerful energy as it merged with mine. He took me in his arms against the warm rocks, and we loved each other intensely deep into the night, as if we had always been one and the same.

The months passed, columns grew among the trees, and I instructed the little one in her future tasks. At night, I loved the man who had come from afar to signal the end of an era. My role did not prohibit me from doing so, as Life revered the sanctity of mortal union when in harmony with the grace of everlasting love. It was a time of deep joy.

But some of the visitors did not approve of this state of affairs, and I saw in their confusion another sign of what She had foretold through my lips. Their ideas about how they wanted to run the sanctuary slowly came forth from the shadows, laden with darkness. And with the passing of time, I came to know that I would never publicly speak another word on Her behalf. The cycle was closing for me. I was Her Priestess and Her body, and it was thus only befitting that I should be sacrificed to usher in the time of decline.

The full moon was setting behind the cliffs as he left. The night was warm and I loved the quiet that preceded dawn, so I stayed out, lying peacefully amongst the wild flowers under my favorite olive trees. All was beautiful and I blissfully closed my eyes. But in a flash, everything changed. I knew they were coming. My instinct stirred, urging me to run or fight with all the fury of a wild beast at the smell of a nearby predator. At the same time, I heard Her voice, as clear as the moon, "Your task is over. Do not fear. You may come back to me now."

I felt pulled between my mortal emotions and the deep Life within, serene and all-knowing, eternal and free. And in that split second of hesitation, they struck.

V

Meeting the Genie

Maya

I opened my eyes and for a few seconds didn't remember where I was. The cave was dark now, the candles having burnt to the ground, but I could still distinguish its interior in the faint beam of light shining through the entrance. I felt rested and my mind was clear, as if the fog that had inhabited me all these months had suddenly lifted. It was amazing. I pulled myself up, squeezed through the narrow crack that served as my door, and cried out with joy at the spectacle awaiting me outside. The sun was setting, and the sky was ablaze with pinks and purples, fading into the dark gray of the coming night.

I swiftly walked towards the fireplace, with a smile in my heart. They were already there, sitting by the crackling flames, wrapped in warm blankets. There was a blanket for me, along with some food laid out on a slate next to the fire: white corn, baked potatoes and grilled cheese. They invited me to sit and eat. What a feast! I felt like I had just been born and was discovering the world for the first time, relishing all that my five senses were delivering. We ate in silence, admiring the flurry of sparks rising up towards the skies.

As the first stars appeared through the black mantle of the night, the Sage spoke.

"Your path has been arduous, but you have found your way back to the land of the ancestors, and we are glad that you are with us now. Initiation into the mysteries of Life entails walking the great labyrinth. The first part of the journey is finding your way in, past the meanders and distractions that could lead you astray, until you find the center, the heart, where lie all the answers about your self. But that is only the beginning. Once you have absorbed the sacred knowledge, then starts the second leg of the journey, which is finding your way back out, carrying the insights that you gained as you were staring into the intense light of your soul.

"On this sacred island, hidden in the folds of the Earth, lies the heart of the labyrinth. If you are willing, you will be taken there. Much will be revealed to you. There will be much to understand and much to experience. And one day, you will step back into the world, transformed."

His words were cryptic, and yet, they brought to mind the vision that had visited me earlier, as I fell asleep in the cave. I understood that I had been walking on this path for a long time and the prospect of somehow getting closer and closer to what he called the heart sent shivers down my spine. It was at once daunting and exhilarating.

"I know that you have come in search for answers," he continued, "in search of healing. To help you, I will take you on a journey into your mind, so that you may better understand your individual story, as well as the collective fate of our time. Your personal story and individual wellbeing are deeply intertwined with the health of our planet – and all of it is purely a matter of what each of us holds in our mind. This will become clear to you. But let us start now, by looking back at the imprints of your footsteps on the soil of time. Tell me your story."

I looked over at Magdalena. She nodded, encouragingly. For the first time in months, I had enough energy to speak, enough clarity of mind to plunge into the memories of my life and share the journey that had brought me all the way to this island.

And so I started. At the beginning.

I spoke long and deep into the night. And when I finally stopped, I stared in silence at the red glow of the embers, lost in my confusion. As I recounted the story of my life under the intense presence of these two wise beings, I almost felt embarrassed at the futility of my professional pursuits, at the unquestioning ardor with which I had sought to earn money and recognition. Nothing seemed to make sense anymore. After some time, the Sage stood up and threw herbs onto the remains of the fire, whispering incantations in a language I could not understand.

"It is not easy to lay out one's life for all to see," he whispered through the smoke. "You have much courage. The courage that is required for the journey. Tomorrow, we will dive in further, beyond the layers that are apparent to you now. You will find that there is more to your story than you thought. And, most importantly, you will come to see how we all manifest our own reality. But for now, you need to get some rest."

He handed me a flashlight and accompanied me to the entrance of my cave. I crawled into my bed, feeling safe and exhausted, thinking about my life and about the words of the Sage.

I found them at the top of the hill the next morning, their long shadows playing with the first beams of light. They greeted me and invited me to sit, Magdalena handing me a steaming cup of herbal tea and a bowl of fresh fruit. She had been right about the healing energy of the island: since we had arrived, some of my bodily symptoms were improving. I no longer felt like an electric current was keeping me awake at night. I no longer felt nauseous and dizzy, and I was able to sleep deeply through the night. I had woken up slightly nervous, not knowing what to expect next, but Magdalena's radiant presence and the stunning beauty of the surroundings quickly reassured me.

"We will start now," the Sage said. And with a smile, he added, "at the beginning."

"Most people believe that their life happens to them. That everything which occurs happens because of external circumstances that are independent of their will. Some people call this fate, others call it God's will, and others choose to call it chance. But regardless of what they call it, they are giving away the responsibility for their lives; they relinquish control over their joys and their sorrows. They become an actor in someone else's play.

"The first thing you need to know is that every single event in your life is determined solely by you, by your unlimited creative capacity. You can manifest beauty and abundance, just as you can manifest cruelty and oppression. You can manifest joy, just as you can manifest suffering. It is up to you, and no one else. You are the director of the play of your life, and you are writing the script with every breath, every thought, every emotion. It is likely, however, that you are not fully aware of the story you are writing. And thus it is easier to believe that external forces come into play.

"And that leads us to the second key: awareness. You may think up a glorious future for yourself, writing the perfect script, and yet experience a life of failure and misery. But that is simply because your thinking mind is not the only one involved in manifesting your reality. At work is the hidden part, the shadow, the subconscious mind. Among its many tasks, it seeks to protect you, by holding on to certain beliefs formed along the journey of your life; beliefs that you are not aware of; beliefs that are busy creating your present. And so, when I talk about awareness of the story you are writing, I am referring to an awareness that opens the door to the deeper layers that make up who you are.

"As we go deeper and deeper, we eventually find a core of pure energy: what our ancestors called your inner Wise One. The part of you, which some might call divine, which lies beyond the limited realms of human experience and connects you to all that is and was and always will be. It is the light of pure knowing and pure being. As it radiates outwards, it meets the other two layers of your mind, subconscious and conscious, where your belief systems are stored and where interpretation takes place. The pure potential from the core starts out unfiltered, uninhibited, unlimited, but as it shines through the outer layers, it takes on form and direction, and a specific reality is created, as determined by the belief systems that it has encountered on its journey. And that reality becomes the story of your life.

"It is only when we become fully aware of the story that we can choose to write a different one."

The Sage paused for a while, giving me a chance to process what he had just said. It was intriguing to conceive of our lives as a sort of play, the script of which lay in our hands. Could it really be that our subconscious beliefs were silently writing the sentences of each forthcoming act?

"Let me illustrate what I mean," he continued, "by telling you a story."

Once upon a time, there was a little girl. And there was a

Genie.

"I grant you three wishes," the Genie magnanimously offered.

"I only need one," the little girl answered as she stood before him, dazzled by his misty heights.

"Are you sure?" he asked, surprised. "That is rather unusual."

"Yes," she said, clear-eyed and innocent.

"Alright then, your wish is my command. I am all ears."

"I want nothing," came the answer, simple, clean, matter-of-fact.

"Nothing?" He couldn't believe his etheric ears.

"Yes, nothing," she repeated.

She was still looking up at him, very earnestly, not at all unsettled by having stumbled upon someone offering to grant all her wishes. She was taking him seriously, without a doubt as to the validity of his existence and his powers. And yet, nothing was the word that came. Nothing. That all-too powerful word.

A tear shone in the corner of the Genie's eye. He had never heard anything like it, but nothing could be done. Indeed nothing had to be done. Her fate had been sealed by the power of the word.

"Your wish is my command," he whispered, and then disappeared.

"Years later, this little girl came to see me. She was a woman by then. And this is her story…

"Whatever she laid her hands on, she ended up losing. Professionally, she was never able to keep a job for more than a few months. She was educated and diligent, hardworking and smart. Yet, in every single job, not long after being hired, something inevitably happened. In some cases, the organization she worked for collapsed under financial difficulties; in others, the team was reorganized and her position eliminated or she would clash with her boss or one of her colleagues. Time after time, no sooner had a few months passed than she was fired or decided to leave because the circumstances had become intolerable. Desperate, constantly searching for something else, she accepted any offer that came her way, even when she was being paid much less than her colleagues, even sometimes as a volunteer. But that made no difference. The very same pattern continued unchanged for years.

"In her personal life, things were not much better. As a young woman, she had many boyfriends, but was never able to hold on to a relationship for very long. Eventually she got married. But it was to an angry, aggressive man, constantly seeking conflict, using every opportunity he could seize to diminish her verbally. She endured it silently, pretending there was nothing wrong, until one day, unable to continue witnessing her suffering, her sister had come and forcibly moved her out. Shortly thereafter, the husband had vanished without leaving a trace. Since then, she had lived on her own, engaging in unsatisfactory short-term relationships. She had many friends, but an honest analysis quickly revealed that most of these friendships were entirely one-sided, and she was always on the giving side. As for her large family, apart from her sister with whom she had a very close, though at times tense relationship, since her aunt's death she had severed all contact with anyone else.

"When she came to see me on this very island, she was at a loss about what to do with her situation. She seemed a kind-hearted and generous woman, yet beneath it all, I sensed a deeply engrained fear. She didn't think her life had been devoid of opportunities. Building a loving family, having a meaningful job and achieving financial stability had appeared perfectly within her reach. Yet, the further she had walked down the path of her life, the faster it had all drifted through her hands, like grains of sand trickling through the cracks, vanishing without a sight. 'There is nothing left in my life,' she had concluded as we sat by the crackling fire. 'Nothing. I don't understand it.'

"'What do you want?' I had asked her.

"She had stared at me in silence, surprised by my question. 'I don't know,' she had answered, shaking her head. 'I have never wanted anything for myself. I have spent my whole life in service to others, willingly giving of myself.'

"The truth of it was that she actually didn't know what it meant to want something. Like many women, she had spent her life putting others before her, putting others' needs before her own. She was quite proud of her selflessness, her devotion and dedication, her generosity. She even went so far as calling it egolessness, an ultimate act of self-sacrifice for the benefit of all. When occasions lent themselves to it, she was not afraid to proudly declare that she had no needs. She saw this as a laudable trait, a quality valued by society. She thought she was spiritually more evolved because she had relinquished her personal needs for those of society at large.

"In reality, she was deeply confused. And this is where the subconscious beliefs come into the picture. In her case, the source of her selfless attitude had nothing to do with generosity, it stemmed from a belief she had formed as a child, which went like this: *I believe I deserve nothing, because I believe I am worthless.* In other words, she believed that she was not entitled to have any needs of her own. She believed that looking after herself when others were in need was shameful. She could not serve her own needs given these had been exterminated. Thus, she concluded that the whole purpose of her existence was to serve others and satisfy their needs, whatever those may be, whatever suffering she might subject herself to in the process.

"She was, of course, not consciously aware of this. You see, we form beliefs based upon events that occur starting in our very early childhood, often when we are still in the womb. Events are neutral in themselves, but we assign a meaning to them, we interpret them as they arise, according to the prevailing circumstances, thus forming specific beliefs. These are then stored in our subconscious, and whenever we are faced with a new event in our lives, our mind refers to our accumulated beliefs and triggers the corresponding emotional reaction. In her case, a series of past events had led her to conclude that she had no value. Over time, circumstances had reinforced this belief, until it was so deep and so strong that it became a reference point for everything in her life. Subconsciously, 'I deserve nothing' soon became 'I want nothing', leaving her standing empty-handed, with nothing to claim as her own.

"I wanted her to see through her confusion by becoming aware of the beliefs she held about herself and realize that these were detrimental and unfounded. I wanted her to understand that not only was it acceptable to have needs and to want something in one's life, it was even inevitable, for wanting 'nothing' was also a desire. It was a heavy spell that she would certainly not have wished upon anyone else. Yet she was inflicting it upon herself; she was manifesting it in her life. For her to grasp this at a deep level and see the little girl standing before the Genie declaring she wanted nothing, we opened the door into her subconscious.

"In doing so, we resurfaced long-buried painful memories of her childhood. Countless scenes of her as a little girl standing terrorized before an angry father screaming that she was good for nothing. Her mother was always around in those moments, but she never said anything, silently going about her tasks, acting as if her daughter was transparent, as if she didn't exist. Very quickly, unable to interpret the situation any other way, the little girl internalized the belief that she indeed was good for nothing, that she was worthless, that she did not deserve to be loved.

"In one of these episodes she remembered most vividly, she had been playing in her room with a doll – a present from her aunt. Her father came in asking why she wasn't helping her mother prepare dinner. He yanked the doll out of her trembling hands, screaming, 'Shame on you! How can you be so selfish and only think about yourself, when your mother needs you!' And thus, in the child's mind, her simple desire to play became associated with shame and fear. Having fun was forever labeled as 'selfish', frowned upon and ejected from the realm of acceptable behaviors. The child's mind had already concluded that she did not deserve to be loved, this last episode suggesting that the affection she craved could perhaps still be gained by doing something for others.

"She and her younger sister were given countless chores to do around the house and beyond. And she wholeheartedly embraced them, finding respite from her abusive home by helping out the neighbors and other family members, and receiving praise in exchange for her work. One morning, she showed up at her aunt's house with a bruised face, shamefully trying to hide the evidence of her punishment under her locks of hair. This triggered a series of heated discussions between the adult members of the family. She wasn't present and didn't know exactly what happened, but from then on, she and her sister lived with her aunt, out of reach of her father's anger, removed from her mother's helplessness. But by then, in spite of her aunt's kindness, her early beliefs had already solidified, laying down the tracks that would direct her life.

"She grew up striving to please all those around her, giving of herself constantly, hoping that she would thereby never again have to face the mistreatment inflicted by her father. She found an identity in the act of giving, effacing herself willingly in the process. But her devotion stemmed not from selfless love, it was born of fear and shame. It was the mechanism she had found to receive love and approval. There was always someone in need, always a hand ready to receive. And she was there, ready to give them everything she had: her time, her mind, even her body.

"Wherever she went, she unknowingly looked at the events in her life through this belief system she had formed as a child. Each sentimental loss she suffered, each job that vanished, each friend who didn't answer her calls simply validated and reinforced her belief that she deserved nothing. The voice in her subconscious said: *You see, once again, it didn't work. I told you so. It's because you're no good; you don't deserve anything. Why don't you stop desiring things? You'll only be disappointed.* It was a vicious circle. Each event and associated interpretation formed an additional layer in the crystalized structure of beliefs that created the experience of her life, spiraling her deeper and deeper into confusion and suffering.

"For her to manifest a different reality, she needed to see her confusion and understand that she had value, that she was allowed to have needs of her own, and that she was allowed to honor them. She needed to learn that she would not be punished if she put her own needs before everyone else's. She needed to learn that the approval and love she was seeking through her selfless behavior could actually only come from within. Indeed, loving herself was not shameful; on the contrary, it was the starting point for everything else. For genuine love could not arise out of shame and fear, but only emerge from the bottomless depths of a soul anchored in the bliss of its luminous essence.

"And that is what we did. She was able to transform her whole life by acknowledging and changing her deep-seated beliefs about herself and her value, and by learning to articulate and honor her needs. As a result, within a year, her life had become unrecognizable: she had a harmonious loving intimate relationship, a stable and interesting job, and she was firmly anchored in a newly discovered feeling of self-acceptance and self-love.

"We will talk more about the actual transformation process. But for now, what I wanted to show you with this story is that the magic and mystery lie in the simple truth that we are the masters of our lives, that we have the ability to change our circumstances and that it is as simple as changing our mind at the deepest level.

"You see my dear Maya, we all have a genie living inside our mind who desperately wants to grant all our wishes. This genie takes every desire formulated by our belief systems absolutely literally. But we are usually unaware of our deepest wishes; they are the result of our confusion and conditioning, our fear and our shame. Thus, it is by shining the light upon them, that we may dissolve the confusion, consciously take responsibility for the creative force alive within us, and manifest the desires we truly want to see blossom.

"This afternoon, I will show you how to open the doors into your subconscious and embark upon a journey into the deeper layers of your mind, so that you too may discover the beliefs that lie hidden in its shadows."

I nodded, fascinated, eager to find out more about myself, yet terrified at the prospect of having to face my darkest truths.

VI

Qullasuyu: Cyclical Struggles

Saywa

And then it happened again. Slipping, slipping through the corridors of time, suddenly being spat out into a cold dark cell. I am a man. I am alone. Pacing.

Why did they leave me here? Where have they gone? Something is going to happen, but I don't know what it is. If only they would tell me. If only someone would come and get me out. It's not too late. It's still possible. I am cold. These bare stones. Damp. I am afraid. What will happen to me? I should have been more careful. How could he betray me? The bastard. I am sure it was him. I knew I shouldn't have trusted him. As if somehow, we had crossed paths before. I should have listened to my intuition.

Pacing now. Keeping warm, despite the pain. I will survive. Something will happen in my favor. Keep pacing. Just keep pacing. I will make it. I always have. So many years of fighting. It can't be the end already. We are not finished. We have only just begun. It started so well. We were so close. Perhaps we can still make it. Perhaps they are claiming victory right now and someone will come. Someone will open the door of this cell and bring me the good news.

I am so thirsty. How long have I been here? What time could it be? I want to know what is happening out there. They must not give up. They must continue. Even without me. They can't give up now. She is still out there. She can lead them. She was always smarter than me. So much stronger. Nothing I can do from here. Trapped like a beast in the dark. Holding on to life with all my strength. My anger. My thirst for revenge.

Pacing. I have to keep pacing. No matter what. These shivers. The throbbing pain. I can't give up. Not now. I can't let myself lie down on this bare floor. It's too cold. I must continue. Continue pacing. They will send help soon. They will succeed. Someone will come. Someone must come.

I am on the floor. Water. I need water. The cold is biting through my skin into the bone. I am frozen. I can't move anymore. Is my heart still beating? I do not know. I hope they keep fighting. In here, it is no longer possible. My body is giving up on me. It has been too long. No sound, no light, no sign of human life. I am in the dark. I am losing my mind. It is all becoming a blur.

The light. Shadows calling my name. This pain. This intense pain. It seems that it has been with me forever. I can no longer move my hands. Everything is numb. Except the pain. The shadows are growing, dark blue flames on a background of intense light. They are talking to me. Calling my name.

All these images flooding my mind. Scenes from my life. Only a few days ago. A sound waking me in the middle of the night. I jump up, but it is too late. A man stands before me, holding a gun to my chest, his face hidden under a black hood. I know who it is. Then the pain. So much pain. And the darkness. Coming to my senses in this pit. I will fight until the very end.

The images take me back in time. I stand on the hill overlooking the city with my companions. They are dying of hunger in there. We know it. We can hear it. It has all gone quiet. Not a chicken is left. Not a donkey. Not even a dog. No sound for months now. And the smell. The stench of death. They should never have come. They should never have humiliated us as they did. This is our land. All we wanted was peace. It was their doing. They asked for it. And now we are almost there. So many months holding the siege. Soon, we will have exterminated them and recovered our land. Recovered our dignity.

I see us, as we launch the first assault. We are strong. More and more brothers and sisters coming to join in the fight. Hearing their battle cry as we march onto the city. Rejoicing together as we seal our first victory. We've made it. No one can leave anymore. No one can come in. We will hold the siege for as long as is needed. I am proud of my people.

I see myself standing outside the great cave on the sacred island, waiting, wondering how many will come. I called those who were still close to the wisdom of our ancestors, the only ones who knew where it was, who were trustworthy in my eyes. We all go inside to receive the blessings from our elders, our teachers in the sacred knowledge of balance and harmony. They look at us with saddened eyes; they know they cannot stop us.

As we stand there together, I feel freedom and an intense reverence for the sanctity of all life. I am suddenly released from my thirst for revenge, expanded beyond my limited self, united with life, serene. The memory of something different. Something pure. It lasts an instant only. A split second of hesitation. But then, the anger floods back in with full strength, pulling me back into my body. I look at my companions. I feel the pulse of their rage united with mine. We want our land back and the only path we see is stained with blood and death. I speak to them and fire up their thirst for justice. And that is when we make the choice that will seal our fate: the great siege of the city.

My wife's eyes looking into mine, shining with passion and determination. The sound of hooves on the soft earth as we gallop together through the high plains. Her long black hair. The first time we make love. The fierce tenderness of her touch.

The rumors of small uprisings happening all over the region, spreading through the plains like wildfire, sending out sparks igniting our imagination. We know they are afraid, and we know they underestimate us, blinded as they are by their arrogance and delusions of cultural superiority. They have no idea what we are capable of. We have nothing to lose, and we have our guides on our side. Unlike them, pale shadows of human beings, we are still in touch with the other side.

I see myself as a young man, carried on the shoulders of my companions. They cry out my name. My new name. The one I took on for our fight for freedom. So many of them looking up to me, following my lead. Our determination to succeed. We cannot let ourselves be annihilated. We cannot let them continue raping our women and desecrating our culture. It is time to end this insanity once and for all.

The terror in the eyes of the first man I killed. A wild creature that knows it will die, yet still unwilling to give in, pleading with my soul. Pulling the trigger. Feeling his life vanish before my eyes. Who am I to cut the thread? It had to be done. I want justice. Stealing the weapons. The escape back to the village.

I am only a child. The daily humiliations. The anger rising up within me. The tears of my mother. They are beating me as if I were an animal. I resist. I refuse to work as a slave. The day we had to leave for the mines. The death of my father.

My village before it all started. The bakery. My sling. Running carefree through the fields. The rising sun. The face of my mother. Her smiling eyes. The light. Intense and beautiful, drawing me towards its magnificence.

Relief. Such relief. Waves of indigo blue carry me towards the light. The pain is gone. I am breathing in pure peace. I no longer feel my body. I am floating, dissolving. I am free. A familiar presence next to me. Reassuring. Intense love. Pure bliss.

I opened my eyes, startled. The birds were chirping and the sun was coming in gently through the curtains. I breathed. I moved my toes and fingers. My body was still there, stretching delicately in the bed. It was warm. My limbs were intact, and my senses seemed to be working just fine. I was a woman. I was alive.

Again it had happened. The experience of a life in the times before. Since Maya's all-knowing eyes had ignited the sparks buried deep within my soul, dawn had become a time of great journeys into the past. As I closed my eyes after my nightly shift, I no longer found sleep, but stepped straight through the veil into another state of being, where images came flooding in. I watched and felt, lived and died, witnessing different versions of my self, as they played the play of human life.

I started laughing like a madwoman. Laughing and laughing at the cosmic joke I had stumbled upon. Was this what death was all about? Could it really be true? Dying and starting all over again. Another body. Another story. Again and again, until the circle became spiral and propelled us into another dimension. It was bewildering, beyond what my mind could comprehend. My life suddenly appeared in a new light, melting away any fear of death and bringing greater clarity to my path and purpose.

I marveled at the thought that I seemed to have been born in this land before, playing a part at the time when my people fought to restore the indigenous state of the highlands, the Qullasuyu. Only to come back again a servant to those whose skin was paler than ours. What an irony. As I reflected further, it dawned on me: the characters in my nightly life-visions were always the same. Patterns repeating. The tables turning. Revenge and forgiveness. Killing and being killed. Loving and being loved. It was fascinating.

How could I have forgotten? How could I possibly have dissociated myself to such an extent as to plunge deep into the density of matter and lose touch with the subtle presence that called my name in the dark? But I had finally heard its call, and opened my eyes to the reality of who I had been, who I was, and why I was here.

In that instant, I knew that my time in this house would soon come to an end. Maya had just left us and I was heartbroken to see her go, consoling myself with the felt certainty that we would see each other again many years down the road. And in the meantime, a new phase was starting for me. I had given all my love to these newborn souls, and they had given me back my true self, connecting me to my roots that stretched deeper than I would ever have imagined.

The shores of the sacred lake were calling me. I was intrigued by the vision of the cave: a sanctuary blessed by the ancient ones, on one of the islands. It must still be there, I thought. And if all this was real, I would find it. I wondered about the man who had been my lover in the land of the Oracle. What had happened to him after my death? I had found Maya. What were the chances that I would find him again? Was it too much to hope for? Was I going insane by lending credibility to my visions? Whatever the case, it was worth a try. I waited for the rains to come and go, packed my humble belongings, bade farewell to the kind nuns and our beloved babies, and set off into the unknown.

VII

The Illusion of Separation

Maya

I will always remember that second afternoon on the island. I had long taken to heart the ancient maxim: *Know Thyself.* I even had these words framed, hanging in my living room, in my apartment in the city. Years of study and reading had exposed me to a vast number of philosophies and concepts about the self and the mind, and I had ceased to be easily surprised or impressed. I thought that I knew myself quite well. But that day I understood that we can know things in many ways, and that the intellectual knowing I was accustomed to, born of logical analysis and deduction, was of a completely different nature to the knowledge that flooded me during that first session and would increasingly do so for the rest of my life.

We had shared another simple meal, and I had retreated to my cave to rest for a few hours. I was still weak, but the fevers had subsided and my mind felt clearer. I was no longer depleting myself; on the contrary, every second on the island was soothing, as if the energy was slowly flowing back into my system, drop by drop. When I went back to the clearing, the Sage was alone. He was leaning against the brown hillside and invited me to join him. I was curious, willing to start looking into my own mind.

"Our ancestors have always worked with states of trance," he started. "They called it by different names and induced it in different ways, be it through the use of psycho-active concoctions or hypnosis, meditation or active dreaming, rhythm or dance. Regardless of the means used, the purpose was to open the doors between this world and the other world, between the seen and the unseen. And in the same way, we can use it to peer into the vast landscapes of our mind. Fully aware of all that is occurring, we become a witness, feeling, hearing and seeing what life presents us, without our conscious mind taking control. You may cross the threshold on your own, but when you start, it is helpful to have a guide who can accompany you and support you in deciphering what emerges.

"Before we dive in together, it is important that you set an intention. This will prompt your mind and guide your journey."

The Sage's words acted like a wildfire, burning through my inner darkness. We had barely started, and already I was deeply shaken. I had come to the island in search of healing. And since my arrival, the Sage had been talking about the hidden beliefs that ran our lives. But there was a deeper, more urgent question nagging me since my mother had broken the news of my adoption. "I want to know who I am," I said.

I had no deeper wish, no greater yearning than finding the answer to that question. I remembered how as a child, I had often felt that I was from another planet, looking with wonder and disbelief at the simple things that all those around me took for granted. I had spent many of my early years gazing at the stars and walking through the forest, wondering where I came from. It was not about finding my bloodline, which I had never doubted, even though it was now clear to me that my vastly different origins had certainly contributed to my estrangement. But my desire to know the truth was deeper, more mystical. It was an urge to track the scent of a long-forgotten memory buried in the wild unexplored caverns of my soul.

Over time, I had learned to pretend this longing wasn't there, pretend I was like everyone else, going about a petty materialistic life confined within the walls of religious austerity. I had learned to ignore the instinctual contraction I felt in my body every time I witnessed disharmony and imbalance, be it in words or in deeds. As my mind cancelled out the sensations, my body simply took the tension deeper. It was still there, but I could no longer feel it. And thus, not only did I no longer resist what I heard and saw that seemed counter to the melody of my soul, I embraced and even started defending the world views that had once seemed so absurd. Meanwhile, unbeknownst to me, my body kept feeling the disconnect, taking it deeper and deeper, in a slow process of self-destruction.

Suddenly, in the smooth transparent light of the high plains, as I pondered the depth of the question that my mother's confession had brought up for me, the extent of my alienation became all too clear. It was as if my long months of illness had acted as a sponge, wiping clean the opaque slate of my mind. I saw all the details of my life and of those who had been around me: their words, their theories, the way people chose to lead their lives, individually and collectively, the greed and destruction, pain and suffering. I gasped in disbelief. Was this what it meant to be a human being? Were we just a collection of misguided beliefs, hurting ourselves and each other because of our confusion? Or was there more? And if so, what was this 'more'? Who was I? Why was I here?

And so, we started. I closed my eyes, and the Sage led me into my mind. I fell deep into trance and the images came flooding in, crisp and clear.

I see myself from above. A newborn baby. My mother is carrying me through the night. I am awake. I can feel that something is going to happen. Her heart is tight, beating fast. I am afraid. The sound of a squeaking shutter. She gives me a kiss and puts me down. She doesn't look at me. She turns away and she is gone. She is gone. I have a dreadful feeling that she will never come back. I am terrified. Did she really leave me? What have I done wrong? Doesn't she love me? Why did she leave?

Why am I here? I didn't want to come back into a human body. It is cold and dark and now I am alone. I am alone. A woman has picked me up. Thank God she found me. She is looking at me. I know her so well. Where have I seen her before? I cannot remember. I am silent. I stare into her eyes. Something special is happening. She too recognizes me. I love her very deeply.

I see myself at eight weeks old, in the same courtyard in the daytime. The sun is shining. A man and a woman are bending over me, smiling, making strange noises. What are they trying to say? They look happy. They are picking me up. They don't seem to have any intention of putting me back down. Oh no, here we go again. Where is my second mother? I can't see her with my face stuck in this woman's arms. Why isn't she here? It is her I want to be with. She is part of my family. Where are they taking me? Don't tell me this is happening again. Could she really be abandoning me as well? How is this possible? What have I done? What's wrong with me?

The vision shifts abruptly. I see myself as a little girl, skipping in the foggy fields. My shoes are wet. I am fascinated by the silvery droplets of rain caressing the fresh green blades of grass. Smiling with joy. A man is calling me. My father. My shoes and dress are soaking wet. He is angry. He wants me to come in. Why do I always have to come in when I'm happy? Perhaps I don't deserve to be happy. I don't know what it is, but I know there is something wrong with me. If I am not careful, they will abandon me again. I must try harder. Perhaps if I try harder, they will love me. Perhaps if I try harder, they will keep me.

The vision shifts again, becoming more abstract. I hear myself calling, 'Who am I? Who am I?...' I see myself in a pale grey-blue cube. My words resonate against the walls. I keep calling out my question, hands cupped around my mouth, 'Who am I?'

I look up. The cube folds away, and now everything around me is dark. Black as the night. Suddenly I see shapes coming towards me, and I understand that they are individual souls. They come in throngs out of the darkness to answer my call; their bodies like flames, shimmering in the dark.

I call again, 'Who am I?' The darkness has become thick with these strange flames, permeated with the eerie glow of their bluish white lights. I am standing in front of them. I look down and suddenly see that my feet are bare and in the sand, as if I was standing on the seashore. Before me is what appears to be a sea of souls, rolling in, wave after wave, from the dark corners of the universe, sending sparks of gold to reflect in my eyes.

I am confused. 'Who am I?' I keep calling. All is silent. Suddenly the golden baroque frame of a gigantic mirror is placed on the edge of the water, between them and me. I look into the mirror and I see the oceanic mass of souls watching me, sending me back the reflection of who I am. More and more of them keep coming every second. They are like droplets of light, undifferentiated, yet separated from each other by a thin silvery contour. The intensity of their light rises as they stare at me. 'What does this mean?' I ask, and look up at the dark sky.

As if answering my call, the vision changes again, and the little flames become a single layer vibrating at the surface of a sphere; a sphere that gradually takes on the features of the Earth. Their contours evaporate: the souls have merged. Through the mirror, I now see a golden layer, a thin mist, pulsating in unison around the planet. I am standing in the darkness of the universe, looking into the mirror at the spectacle of who I am. I reach through the frame, open my arms and embrace my reflection: the Earth along with the myriad souls vibrating as one at her surface. I hold the Earth against my heart, and feel Her heart beating with mine. Slowly, the misty layer of souls funnels into my heart, along with the planet. All vanishes inside me to the rhythm of one all-encompassing beating heart.

In our united pulse arises an overwhelming vibration of love, an intense wave of shining light. It comes suddenly, powerfully spreading through my whole being and beyond, bathing me in its ecstatic golden glow. My whole body is shaking. It is more joy than I have ever experienced. More beauty than I have ever known. I recognize it as the very fabric of my being. And then, very clearly, I hear the words.

'You are Energy refining itself.
You are Love experiencing itself.
You are Life becoming more.'
I wish I could stay in this state forever.
'You can.'
Slowly, the intensity fades and the voice of the Sage brings me back.

I opened my eyes, squinting, feeling shaky, in between worlds. The Sage was sitting by my side, smiling.

"Come," he said, "Let's go for a walk. It will help you come back into this world." We walked slowly, in silence, on the little path that meandered its way along the hillcrests, through the brown grass, accompanied by the vastness of the horizon. Our shadows grew longer. Birds cried in the distance. The path circled around gently and brought us back to the base of the highest hill, from whence, with the last rays of the sun, we ascended to the top, through the stone circle and back to the fireplace.

The fire was lit. Magdalena was preparing dinner, her golden face glowing through the flames. She looked up at me, warmly, knowingly. I felt light and at peace, and at the same time unsettled, as if I had just been given the pieces of a puzzle called Myself, which I didn't yet know how to assemble fully, which I didn't yet dare to embrace completely because it meant shaking the very foundations of my being and deconstructing everything my ego had spent so many years creating and holding on to.

"The question you asked is the most important one: 'Who am I?' It is from here that everything else unfolds," the Sage said. "It is true: *'You are Energy refining itself. You are Love experiencing itself. You are Life becoming more…'* That's what we all are. And yet, we walk through life in a state that is vastly different from the ecstatic bliss you have just experienced, a state we could call the state of separation. Nearly all humans feel as if something were missing in their lives. Usually, we are not even aware of it, but this feeling that we are lacking something, that we are not whole gnaws at us from within, manifesting in our lives in different ways. This is the pain of separation: a throbbing wound opened again every single time we believe that by coming into a body we have been cut from our divine essence. We slash it open again every single time we embrace the thought that we have fallen from grace, that we have been banished from the Garden of Eden because of the primordial sin of being human. As long as we hold these beliefs, the pain of separation will never be soothed. We can only heal it by discovering the truth about who we really are.

"But this can be a long journey. And thus, most of us believe that the pain we feel has to do with human separation. We believe that our feeling of incompleteness is due to insufficient love and affection, and that we may be mended if we earn the approval and appreciation of others. We believe that others can give us back what we think we have lost. And we spend our entire lives trying, running after a goal that remains forever out of reach. All of this is a complete fallacy arising from the depths of our confusion about the true nature of our being. In the unlimited reality of our higher self, there is only connectedness and bliss. There is nothing missing. There is nothing outside of ourselves. You already are all that you think you are lacking. And much, much more."

'You are Love.' How many times had I heard people casually utter these words? As though saying them was a panacea to the malaise of our time. But now, I wanted to say them myself. They were no longer mere words: they were a lived reality, and that made all the difference. But I understood that this reality could not be forced, it could not be willed nor induced. It could not even be communicated. It could only be experienced. In the church of my childhood, they would have said: by the grace of God. Yes, this was grace indeed. Something that came flooding in when one least expected it, provided the gates were open.

And I remembered sitting in my father's church, listening to the organ and stepping through into the dream-world. I realized that I had spent most of my childhood entering states of trance in the blink of an eye. The world of joy and union I had experienced had been real. It was the world beyond the illusion of separation. I had known then. I had always known. Could it really be that I had mentally dismissed and then forgotten my childhood experiences of oneness, because I wanted to please those who provided for me? Because I was afraid that if I didn't comply with their worldview and their wishes, they might abandon me yet again?

Echoing my inner questioning, the Sage continued, "In your life, you have been torn between the truth alive within you, and a seemingly contradictory reality projected onto you by the outer world since the very first weeks of your life. The baby that you were could never understand why your birth mother would abandon you. There you were, innocently yearning for motherly love, and before you knew it, she was gone. The only explanation your infant mind could find was that you were the problem, that there was something wrong with you. And thus you formed the belief that you were unlovable. You were cared for by Magdalena for several weeks, but she again passed you on to other hands. This was another inexplicable mystery for your infant mind. It reinforced your initial belief that nobody wanted you, that there must be something wrong with you, and from this point onwards, you suffered from an intense fear of being abandoned by those you needed for your survival, by those you loved.

"Because of where you come from, the ancestral knowledge is strong within you, and as a child, you spontaneously had experiences that plugged you right back into the source, into states of utter bliss where the thought of being unlovable was completely absurd. But the culture you were brought up in pulled you further and further away from these experiences, discrediting them as mere fantasy. Thus, as the joyful experiences of your dream-world were frowned upon, you started doubting their validity.

"Over time, your fear of abandonment had the upper hand, and you negated the reality that was alive within you. No longer watered by your internal fountain of bliss, you had to turn to the external world to quench your thirst. You were impelled to behave in such a way as to please those around you to make sure they would not leave you again. As you slipped into adulthood carrying the child's beliefs with you, you walked further and further away from what you felt and knew, until you could no longer feel nor know through your body. And no matter how hard you tried, the pain of separation only kept growing. Your longing could never be satisfied.

"We all carry a version of that story within us. The story of confusion and separation. The belief that we do not deserve to be loved, that we are not good enough. But our bodies are never confused. They always know what is going on, and thus, when the self-inflicted pain born of our confusion reaches its zenith, our bodies sometimes break down to give us an opportunity to see our life as it really is. If we don't pick up the challenge, well… we simply die, and start again in another life."

He paused. The full moon was rising above the lake, its silvery reflection glistening over the still waters.

"You found your way here, because your inner connection started stirring again, rising from the ashes of a failing body and an exhausted mind. And also, because words have power, and your name was well chosen. Your birth mother left you a precious gift. A token of her immense love and capacity to see far and deep."

"My name?" I asked.

"Yes. Your name. In our language, Maya means 'One'. And in the ancient language from across the seas, Maya means 'the veil of illusion'. By carrying this name, you are embracing the reality of both within you simultaneously: the experience of oneness and the veil that withholds us from that very experience. Your name is a metaphor of the human condition and its dormant potential. As Maya, you may break through the illusion of our limiting beliefs into Oneness."

I didn't sleep that night. I sat for a long time at the entrance to my cave. I was shocked by what I had seen about myself and my earliest beliefs, by the realization that these had stayed with me to this very day. How could it be that I really believed myself to be unlovable? It was appalling. I had never considered myself as someone prone to low self-esteem, blindly driven by an intense fear of rejection. And yet, here was clear evidence suggesting the contrary. It was deeply revealing and utterly disturbing, especially when seen in the light of the profound feeling of bliss I had experienced in the second part of my journey in trance.

I admired the shadows cast by the full moon as it journeyed slowly through the sky, listening to the muffled sounds of the night. In this light, the world seemed so different; there was a silvery glow to all things, a possibility of magic, of breaking through the limitations imposed by our mind. Were all limitations really created by our mind? Were we truly unlimited, infinite, eternal? Why was it so hard to feel that reality in our lives, beyond getting a glimpse every now and then? How could we sustain that feeling and anchor its very vibration into our everyday experience?

As the moon set behind the mountains, I retreated into the warm serenity of my cave. I had started to enjoy the cocoon-like feeling that I experienced inside. I continued thinking about separation, the illusion of separation. And as I lay down in my bed, I felt softly held by the Earth, permeated by a subtle pulse of deep love and awareness.

Was it really as simple as changing my mind?

VIII

Exclusivity of Thinking

Maya

We went for a walk the next morning, on a path that cut straight down through the fields, all the way to the lake. We walked along the rocky shores for a while until we reached a small cove sheltered from the wind. Clouds were hanging low over the waters, draping us in a mysterious cottony veil. It was as if we were on a lost continent, in another world.

I lay down on the pebbles and closed my eyes. As I rested, the Sage spoke as if he had heard my question from the night before. As if we had been in a continuous dialogue, interrupted only by the majestic breath of nature flowing through us, as we reverently took her in.

"Yes," he said, "it is as simple as changing our mind. But there are many layers to our personal reality. We have only just started. What you saw and understood yesterday is an important facet, but there is more. There is much more. While it is in seeing our confusion and understanding at the deepest level that there is no separation that we get to the root of the problem, our understanding is often only partial. The challenge lies in holding on to the new insights we have gained and not reverting to former patterns and behaviors, which ultimately pull us back into the grip of our past erroneous beliefs about who we are.

"The reason this is a difficult hurdle to overcome, is because the ego is built in such a way as to do everything to hold on to and reinstate the familiar. We are afraid of the unknown, of leaving behind all that is familiar, even if it means suffering. That is why many people are unable to leave destructive relationships, unhealthy environments, or abusive bosses. They may have seen and largely changed their innermost beliefs about their own value. They may have understood that they deserve to be loved and respected. But the transformation is usually not absolute. And when they step back into their old lives and are faced with the practical complexities of changing past patterns, the tentacles of the familiar are too strong to resist, and their minds soon find justification in thinking that the status quo is not that bad after all.

"When we walk the labyrinth out from the center and back into the world, the key is to slow down and observe our minds, observe every single one of our decisions, observe what we say yes to and what we say no to, observe what we give our energy to. It is by slowing down that we become aware of how deep certain patterns have run and are able to steer our course in accordance with our newly established beliefs, with what we have come to know about ourselves. By slowing down we can build our inner clarity and strength to find our way out, leaving the shattered remains of our discarded past behind us.

"Let me share another story to illustrate what I mean. A story that may seem extreme in certain ways, but whose patterns are by no means unique."

"There was a man who once came to see me, as I was travelling through his city. He hoped that with my help, he would be able to change his life. The fact that he came was an important sign that his desire to live, though flailing, was still there. But the pattern of self-loathing he brought was deeply engrained, and I knew that for him to manifest a different future would take very strong willpower and total commitment. It always does, but sometimes, the road is more arduous.

"It all started in his early childhood. A few years after his birth, his father left for another woman, forsaking any responsibilities for his son. His mother raised him on her own, devoured by a deep sense of failure. She was hurt as a woman, ashamed to have been replaced by another. She felt rejected, unloved, deeply alone. And she felt guilty towards her son, because she had failed to give him the perfect father she had dreamed of.

"But here was a little baby who looked into her eyes with unconditional love, who seemed to whisper: you are perfect as you are. Needing a conduit for her unrequited feelings, she fully immersed herself in the vast universe of motherly love and devotion, a place of grace where all else vanished, where she experienced a depth and quality of love she had never known possible.

"She spent all her spare time with her child. As he became older, she started sharing her thoughts and feelings with him, her daily concerns, her inner doubts. She spoke to him as one speaks to a partner, as if she were asking him to grow up fast so that he could replace the man who was no longer by her side. Unknowingly, she was expecting him to fulfill her emotional needs, and redeem her into lovability. She desperately clung to the embrace of the mother-child cocoon, blindly praying for immutability, pretending not to notice the passing of time. Meanwhile, her latent feelings of shame and guilt kept working in the shadows, slowly painting a layer of sadness over her life.

"His mother was everything to him. She had spared no effort, no sacrifice for his wellbeing. His ultimate reward was to see her happy. And just as he had assumed responsibility for his father's disappearance, he felt responsible for his mother's unhappiness. He did everything in his power to make her smile. Alas, all his efforts proved vain.

"In this entanglement of two well-intentioned, yet misguided beings, his subconscious belief of not being good enough was born. He could not meet her emotional needs. He could not replace the man she had lost. In fact, her suffering could not be soothed by a man's love. It was deeper, it was the pain of the primordial wound, the illusion of separation caused by her confusion about the true nature of her divine being. But the little boy tried. And the more he tried, the more he faced failure, seeing the carefree joy of his childhood slipping away, ultimately arriving into adulthood devastated at his incapacity to bring lasting happiness to the one he loved most.

"This pattern of taking responsibility for others' happiness and subconsciously choosing situations that reinforced his belief that he was a failure played out in all his intimate relationships. He was a kind, good-looking man who easily met women. Yet he was attracted to women who, like his mother, turned to him to fill a gaping hole, to soothe their loneliness and their throbbing pain. And with every single one of them, he tried, even though he knew that it was futile, not because he recognized that their demands were unrealistic, but because his mind whispered: *You're a failure. You do not deserve this woman's love. Besides, you are unable to make any woman happy. You already know that. Just look at your mother. Why do you keep on trying? This woman will realize this soon enough. And she will leave you, once again.* In spite of this, the relationship sometimes lasted for years, as both partners clung to their illusions. But ultimately, the women ended up proclaiming their unhappiness and leaving, whilst he declared defeat.

"He found comfort in drink and various intoxicants. Initially, they took him to other worlds, where all seemed possible, where he felt less inhibited, less limited. Where he regained hope in life and in himself. Over time, however, the bottle lost much of its exhilarating effect and became a monotonous aid to getting through the days, a faithful friend to lean on, reliable and constant. It was there to numb his suffering and dull his senses, taking him deeper and deeper into the slumber that he had initially tried to escape.

"He had wanted to be an artist and from what he told me, it seemed that he was quite talented as a young man. But there too, the pattern had planted its teeth. He was convinced that he would never make it. And thus, he didn't even try. He had never completed his degree at art school and stopped painting long ago, working the odd temporary job, barely getting by. He lived in the same block as his mother, still spending much time with her, seeking escape in the remnants of their cocoon, a floating mirage of absolute love in a sea of mediocrity and self-destruction.

"He came to see me as a man in his fifties. He had recently met a woman who rekindled his desire to live, his desire to love and be loved. He wanted to be with her. This time, he really wanted to make it work. Yet he felt he had nothing to offer. His health had been seriously impaired by years of drinking; his financial situation was a disaster. One night, in a bar, as he lucidly contemplated his life, wondering whether it could still be different, he met a man who knew me, who told him how he had transformed his life after journeying into his mind. And that is how we started working together.

"When I first saw him, he already knew a lot about his condition and the devastating effects it had on his life. He knew that his health was failing rapidly and that early death was a near certainty. He had tried to stop drinking several times, but always ended up finding excuses for his incapacity to do so, slipping back into past patterns, uncovering new arguments to reinforce his belief that he was a failure.

"We spent a lot of time exploring the origin of his addiction. I took him back to his childhood. In trance, he saw himself walking home from school, finding his mother locked in the bathroom, crying. He was still a child and assumed that it was because of him, that he had somehow misbehaved, missed an opportunity to bring her joy. He felt responsible for her despair and pledged to do everything in his power so that she would never be sad again. Alas, such scenes had frequently repeated themselves. Looking back, he understood the futility of the endeavor, how he had set himself up for failure and prepared his mind to conclude time after time that he simply wasn't good enough for anything in this world.

"He became intensely aware of how this belief expressed itself in all aspects of his life, both intimate and professional, and how deeply embedded it had become. He saw how consistently it had been reinforced since his early childhood, ultimately resulting in intense self-loathing, leading him to abhor his very existence. Not having the courage to end it once and for all, his mind resorted to drinking and drugs, as a surreptitious attempt at committing slow suicide. Intellectually, it became crystal clear to him that he was trying to kill himself, on the grounds of a deeply held feeling of utter unworthiness.

"In a certain way, seeing it all enabled him to change his mind about himself. By witnessing the birth of his misguided belief system, he saw through his confusion and touched the pure magnificence of being human, of being alive. He understood that he could love himself. He saw how deeply the patterns were interwoven with his being, and how they could be interrupted. After a few sessions together, he left confident and hopeful, determined to break his addiction and change his life.

"His plan was, simply, to believe in himself. Firmly anchored in a newly found self-love, he was determined to stop drinking once and for all, and start painting, venturing slowly in the direction he had always dreamed of. Most importantly, regarding the woman who had ignited his desire for transformation, he intended to engage in the relationship acutely vigilant of any desire to take on responsibility for her feelings. His path was clear and he had laid out in detail his vision for the new life he wanted to create.

"I hesitated to let him go. We had spent little time together and the pattern ran very deep. The belief structures that stemmed from his lack of self-worth were intricate and complex, branching out in many subtle ways. Had we peeled away enough layers? Had he changed his mind sufficiently to hold the new vibration of self-love that would enable him to manifest a different reality?

"I didn't hear anything from him for about six months. Then, one day, a message came, informing me that he was in the hospital, asking whether I would consider working with him again. The message itself was cloaked in shame; the shame he felt at confessing yet another failure. The pattern had not been broken, and there he was, back at the starting point, feeling even worse at having proven once more to himself and the world that he was no good.

"He had been so confident as he left. What happened? Let me take you into his mind, so that you may see for yourself."

We had just finished a simple picnic. I was fascinated by the Sage's story. I imagined the scenes that he described, as if I was seeing them play out before my eyes. The fog had lifted and the sun was sparkling over the still waters. I was intrigued by his invitation.

"Close your eyes," he said, "and focus your energy on the mind of this man, on all that I shared, all that you felt and saw as I was talking. Tell me what you see. Tell me what you feel."

No sooner had the Sage finished his sentence than I saw a man walking through the streets, and I spoke out the vision that appeared before me. The man was in his fifties, wearing a dark coat, walking energetically through the gray suburbs of a big city. He arrived at a clump of identical apartment buildings, sharing a common courtyard, where stray teenagers were smoking cigarettes with a feigned air of nonchalant self-importance. He barely glanced at them and walked in, taking the elevator up to the tenth floor. As he entered what seemed to be his apartment, he sighed deeply. Empty bottles were cluttering the living room table and kitchen counter and a stack of moldy dishes lay abandoned in the sink. The furniture was buried under a layer of sticky dust, and the floors and carpets had taken on an indistinct color. Even to him, it was repulsive.

He took his jacket off and started cleaning ferociously, as if he were cleaning away the past to make way for a different life. After a burst of intense activity, he stopped, exhausted. It was evening and he realized that he had barely started to lift the filth accumulated through years of neglect. And that's when the first moment of self-doubt kicked in.

My vision suddenly went deeper and I was astounded to notice that I could see into his mind and hear his thoughts. His body was urging him to open a bottle of red wine. Yet he was prepared for this, determined to resist, aware of the efforts that would be required to break his habit. He got some juice from the fridge and prepared dinner, attempting to distract his attention by focusing on simple tasks, eating, and reminding himself that his life had value and that he no longer wanted to destroy it.

It worked for a while, but as the evening dragged on, the full reality of pulling through the transformation hit him. He realized that he would need to stay aware of his thoughts and feelings every second, catching any moment of doubt, any self-judgment or criticism, any covert feeling of unworthiness. Change, as it turned out, was a full-time endeavor.

Did he really have time for this? Was it worth it? He thought about the woman he loved. Wasn't it enough that he now loved himself a little more? Wasn't it enough that he understood better the potential pitfalls of a relationship? His mind was agitated, thinking through the challenges that awaited him over the next days and weeks. He picked up the phone and dialed her number.

The vision jumped and I saw them together. They were sitting on a bench in a park, her head resting on his shoulder, a tear rolling down her cheek. She had her arm around his waist embracing him tightly, torn between her existential anguish and her yearning for relief in the arms of a man. He was staring into the distance, lost in thought.

I was shown the scene, while at the same time becoming aware of the broader circumstances. I understood that by holding on firmly to his newly found self-worth, he had successfully stopped drinking. His boosted self-confidence led him to believe that this was all he needed to navigate his former reality in a new more satisfying way.

Alas, while he had gained new insights, and even broken through his addiction to alcohol, the destructive patterns of the past were triggered anew by the woman he loved. She was no different from the many women he had been with in the past. He had vowed to refrain from focusing on keeping her happy, but he didn't know how else to behave. And she, faithful mirror of his mother, constantly begged him for the assurance of his love, as a balm to heal her deeply entrenched feelings of being unlovable and raise her out of her depression.

He had become a keen observer of his mind, and as he sat on the bench in the park, he saw it all very clearly. She had prompted his desire to become free from the past, yet she seemed to pull him straight back into it. How could he escape? He had briefly tried to touch upon the subject and probe into the origins of her neediness, but she had reacted violently, breaking down in tears and accusing him of being insensitive to her suffering. If he stayed with her, there seemed no way out. If he left her, he would lose that for which he had made the changes in the first place. He didn't want to be alone. He no longer abhorred his existence, but the prospect of solitude scared him. He felt deeply attached, unwilling and unable to leave her.

The vision shifted again, taking me to a hospital bed, where he was writing a letter; the letter to the Sage. He seemed much older than in the previous scenes, with a swollen face and sunken eyes, his entire being shrouded in a gray mist of gloom. As he wrote, I saw that he was still fighting. Intellectually, he understood it all. Since moving in with the woman he loved, he had loosened his grip on his own transformation, and was plunged back into the energetic circumstances of his childhood. As had been the case with his mother, open communication became difficult. Faced with his partner's fragility, her constant demands and tearful pleas, his feeling of responsibility had soon come creeping back in, followed by disappointment and helplessness, ultimately raising the specter of unworthiness from its ashes.

As if that had not been enough, his aging mother hadn't been able to recognize his sincere wish to change. When he had proudly announced that he had quit drinking, her snickering response had been, "Really? For how long this time?" She had dismissed his desire to start painting again as a childish waste of time and responded to all his little successes by drowning them in her vast sea of negativity.

Over time, he had let go of his vision and plummeted back into misery, concluding that his attempts were pointless. He had found justification in the thought that his life was simply too hard, that he was not up to the task, and that his current situation was perhaps not that bad after all. He had soon started drinking again, was hopelessly unhappy in his relationship, and eventually ended up in the hospital with a heart-related condition.

I was touched by this man's life, his struggle and his despair, his good intentions and ultimate fall back from grace. And I turned to the Sage, puzzled, "Why didn't it work? I thought you said that we only need to change our mind to transform our lives? Didn't he see his beliefs and change his mind? Didn't he go back with self-love, a carefully thought-through plan, and a keen intention to become an observer of his mind?"

"Yes he did," the Sage acquiesced, pensively. "But there are many layers to our mind. Coming into alignment with a new belief system, with new discoveries about ourselves and our ultimate nature takes practice. It is like a flower bud, freshly born. For it to blossom, it needs just the right combination of sunshine and rain, the right temperature and humidity. If you suddenly were to transpose it back into winter, the bud would never open and freeze to its death. When we come back into the world after an intense look in the mirror, it is essential that we create an environment that supports the new life flowing through our veins. Only thus can we spot the dead-ends and steer our way out of the maze.

"You see, we attract to us the people and situations that reflect our subconscious programming. In other words, even if we are not aware of it, the lives we live are fully resonant with our deepest beliefs. We may step out and change our minds, but if we step back into the very same environment, we are essentially going back to a setting that supports the very thoughts and actions we want to transform. In the early stages of transformation we are often fragile and highly suggestible. We are like an alcoholic who has stopped drinking, but nevertheless goes back to live in a bar, thinking all the while that his willpower is strong enough to pull it through. It may be, but usually, it doesn't work.

"What is required in those cases is strong decisive action to extract ourselves from the familiar yet obsolete environment created by our past value system. We often don't know what will come next, because our new thoughts are only just forming. So it is essential that we give them a neutral space and a chance to mature, until they attract the new people and circumstances that match our modified beliefs about ourselves and the world.

"Why did he move in with this woman despite his awareness that their relationship was dragging him back into his past patterns? Relationships can be a tremendous opportunity for healing, but only when both partners are willing to acknowledge and resolve their projections and fears. As he quickly found out, this was not the case here. So why did he not have the willpower to leave her and be on his own? Why was he still looking for love outside of himself? These are important questions because they reveal the extent to which his mind had really changed. If he had anchored himself firmly in the self-love he said he had found, he would not have felt the urge to engage in a relationship. He would not have been afraid of being on his own. He would have been capable of making clear choices to honor his ultimate wellbeing, even if these choices lay counter to his lingering emotional attachments.

"But what you have seen is not the end of his story. After I received his letter, I invited him to come out to this island. I knew that the commitment involved in undertaking the journey would test his resolve. If he came, he would experience a different setting and have another opportunity to change the course of his life.

"Barely a month passed and he was here. Initially, he doubted how much more we could do together, as he already had a far-reaching understanding of his situation. But it was purely intellectual, almost detached. Intellectually, he knew that he should love himself more. Intellectually, he fully grasped that if he continued on this path, he would most likely die prematurely. But for him to make different choices, his knowledge had to become emotional, it had to become embodied. And for that to happen, I took him to his future."

"Look," the Sage added, making a broad gesture in front of me, as if lifting a curtain, "this is where he went."

I saw the man lying on blankets in a big cave illumined by

torches. The Sage was sitting by his side, inviting him to step forward in time and witness his future. The man surrendered to the Sage's suggestion, slipped into trance, and saw himself six months later, on the eve of his birthday. He was on his own, in the apartment he shared with his girlfriend, sitting on the sofa in front of the television. A glass of wine in his hand, he lethargically stared into the void, reflecting on the passing of time. Suddenly his jaw tightened from the pain in his abdomen, this pain that rarely left him anymore. He knew what it foreshadowed, but chose to pretend it wasn't there.

The doorbell rang. It was his mother, but he didn't get up to open. He couldn't bear seeing her and having to endure her endless stream of criticism. She banged on the door, complaining through the cracks, reminding him that she was helping him out financially, that he was useless and should find a job. But he simply sat there wincing from the pain, waiting for her to go.

The film of his life fast-forwarded and in the next scene, he was in a coma, transported away to the hospital, as a heavy piece of freshly butchered meat, barely holding on to the last thread of life. He watched from above as they connected him to countless drips and machines to prolong the life that he had so assiduously endeavored to cut short.

The thread soon broke, and in the next scene, he saw himself in a cemetery. They were lowering his coffin into a grave. Half a dozen people had gathered, the frail figure of his mother at the forefront, her gray face and clenched jaw hidden under the rim of a black hat. At the back, the woman who had been his beloved was wiping her tears, confused between a guilty feeling of relief and her despair at finding herself alone. A couple of his friends had come, men who shared his sins and resented his death as a chilling sign of what awaited them before long.

The vision deeply disturbed him. The collection of humans standing in a semi-circle around his discarded body was pitiful, appearing to him as faithful mirrors of how he had been: full of self-loathing, fear and confusion. And those who hadn't shown up spoke through their absence. There was no kind word, no beauty, no recent joyful memories of the deceased to be shared. Nothing but an exchange of false platitudes, and a meager bouquet of white flowers wilting rapidly in the dense atmosphere of human suffering that permeated the scene. And that is when the strangling intensity of his pain hit him with full force, an electric shock running through his entire body, pulsation after pulsation. For the first time in decades, tears formed in his eyes, and he was filled with an overwhelming feeling of sadness for having wasted his life. "This is not what I wanted!" he cried, sobbing uncontrollably.

"Now," the Sage summoned him, his voice resonating from the depths of the cave, "come back to the present and know that everything you have seen exists in potential only. You are standing at a fork in the road. A different future is possible. You have an opportunity to make different choices, to walk a different path."

The man saw himself on a path in the hills, standing at a juncture, shaking. In front of him was a stone-paved road leading down to the bleak scenes he had just witnessed, straight to his death. Slightly to his left, a steep narrow trail wound its way up into the hills.

"The choice is yours. Where will you go?" asked the Sage.

It was as if a light had gone on in his mind. After all this inner work, he had thought that he knew himself, understood his patterns and addictions, and was keenly aware of where his path was leading him. He hadn't expected that it could get any worse. He had thought that death would merely come as a smooth continuation on the journey of his failed existence. But now, having fully experienced the ruthless march of his life, as it descended into pain along the linear path laid by his self-loathing and confusion, he felt as if he had just opened his eyes after a life of walking around in the dark.

He found it hard to believe that anyone would subject themselves to so much suffering, and that they would do so by choice. It was absurd. He didn't want to feel like this anymore. In that instant, his entire belief system based upon his lack of self-love broke into a thousand pieces and fell to the ground, like a discarded suit of armor. With it went all the layers of confusion, his programmed beliefs, his urge to resort to drinking to make himself feel better. He shook it all off, watching it slowly turn to dust and vanish into the ground.

He firmly veered towards the left and took the narrow trail up towards the sun-lit sky. And as he walked, he experienced a different potential future. In the first scene, I saw him in a small apartment with large windows. It was very clean, sparsely but tastefully furnished, full of beautiful natural sunlight. I understood that he was living alone, having ended his former relationship. He was sitting at a table, pleased, contemplating the painting that stood on the easel, and eagerly thinking about the invitation he had just received to exhibit his paintings in a gallery. He smiled, knowing this would be a wonderful chance to move closer to his dream of living from his art.

"And so," the Sage said, his voice dropping the curtain before my vision, "as the futility of his suffering hit him with full force, he instantly embraced new values and experienced a different potentiality, a different life path and a different death."

He paused, giving me time to regain awareness of my surroundings. I drank some water and stared at the lake, digesting the intensity of all I had just witnessed.

After a while, the Sage continued, "I shared this story with you to illustrate how difficult it is to break engrained patterns, and how much it sometimes takes to truly change one's mind at the deepest level. It is not uncommon that we find ourselves in a situation where we think we have changed the beliefs of being unlovable and not being good enough that lie at the core of our self-destructive tendencies. But we need to remember that these beliefs manifest in many ways and have to be tackled from different angles. As long as an inkling of identification with these thoughts remains, the fragment of a doubt, they will continue to be creative and manifest situations in our lives that send us back their very image.

"Our path of coming into wholeness implies reaching what we could call exclusivity of thinking, which means that our understanding of our divine essence is absolute. This entails both an intellectual and an embodied emotional understanding of who and what we truly are. It means consistently and unwaveringly holding the vibration resonant with that understanding: the vibration of pure love. When we maintain this state, nothing can distract us, harm us or scare us. Nothing can dampen our creative potential. Nothing can send us sliding back into the throngs of our doubts and self-loathing. In such a state, the external circumstances we walk into do not touch us, for they are immediately transformed by our presence.

"This is our potential. It is towards this exclusivity of thinking that we are all evolving. But along the path, our attention gets distracted, we become confused and have the opportunity to experience our thoughts, whatever they may be, as they take form creating the circumstances of our lives. We create, we experience, we observe and we correct our course. And thus, as we walk the journey, it helps to choose supportive environments, which will sustain our progress and send us spiraling faster and faster towards the full recognition of our divine essence."

The Sage stopped talking and leaned back against the rocks. I listened to the birds cry as their shadows passed over ours. I played with the smooth pebbles, letting them run through my fingers. And I looked into the Sage's deep knowing eyes. Everything was becoming transparent. I felt in harmony with the world and with myself, grateful at having caught a deeper glimpse of the human destiny through the parted curtains of the mind.

And I wondered: how does all of this apply to me?

IX

Willakuti:
The Return of the Sun

Saywa

I had left the city on the eve of the winter solstice, our new year. Before searching for the big cave on the island, I wanted to go back to my village and to the ancient ruins, where the celebrations were being held to welcome the return of the sun. I was filled with excitement and a tinge of apprehension. Would I find anyone I knew after so many years? Would the land I had loved be abandoned?

The bus travelled down the fast road through the vast plains, bringing back the painful memories of me as a little girl journeying in the opposite direction with tears in my eyes. It seemed so long ago. Before I knew it we stopped, the driver pulling me out of my nostalgic reverie by announcing the name of my village. I got off on the roadside, alone, and turned towards the dusty street leading to what had been my home. A cool wind was blowing. The eternal snows glistened in the distance. The air was fresh and dry, and the sight of the brown hills warmed my heart. Save for the animals, which I could not see anywhere, it seemed that nothing had changed.

I gathered my courage and walked down to the clump of houses hugging the hillside. A dog barked, a hopeful sign that it was still inhabited. An old man with missing front teeth was sitting on a bench against a stone wall. He had spotted me from afar and was waving at me. I reached him with a beating heart, took his hands and told him my name. His face lit up. He remembered me. "Saywa," he said, "can this really be…?" And then he added, "Your llamas. I cared for them all these years. The old ones died, new ones were born. Come, I will show you." Steadying himself on his cane, bent over from years of labor, he took me around the back. And there, sure enough, a small flock of llamas was grazing in a large pen. They raised their long necks and cocked their ears, suspicious of the stranger I had become.

It was unbelievable. How could it be that after so much time, having experienced such dramatically different circumstances in the city, I could come back to a place where everything had remained the same? It made me so happy that I wanted to embrace him. We gathered the half-dozen old men and women who still lived in the village and sat outside on the wooden benches, in a roofed spot shaded from the intense sunlight. Someone brought out a big pot of the hot purple corn drink that I loved, and we chatted merrily as if we had always remained together. How I had missed this life.

None of them had any news from my parents, nor my brothers and sisters who had never come back. The young people had all left for the city, they explained, except for the few who worked at the ruins, which were receiving a growing number of visitors. Life was hard; the crops were all but abandoned, save the essential potatoes, quinoa and corn. They could just get by, with the help of their children and grandchildren who came back on the bus every now and then, bringing with them the bare necessities.

They didn't ask me about my life in the city. Perhaps they knew how easily the illusions of greatness that had lured our people away could be shattered, replaced by the dire reality of urban poverty and discrimination, in the clutches of which most of us had ended up. Perhaps they knew that our deep longing to return was ultimately extinguished by our shame. Yet they held no judgment, anchored deep in their wisdom and the simple profound ways of the mountains. As the sun started setting on the horizon, I bade them farewell, explaining that I wanted to walk towards the ruins and spend the night of the Willakuti there, in a ritual that to me symbolized not only the coming of a new year, but the beginning of a new life. They sent me off with their blessings, and the heartfelt invitation to come back and stay, should my new life lead me this way.

I walked for a couple of hours in the direction of the ruins. It was getting dark, but I remembered exactly where they were; the trail we had often followed with my grandfather still seemed in use and in the distance I could see a faint light, a fire perhaps. I felt like I was walking towards my past, in search of an archaic heritage that cut across cultures and peoples and would reconnect me to the very essence of my soul. It was almost a year since Maya's eyes had opened the door. I knew deep inside that this pilgrimage of sorts would help me tie the loose threads I had experimented with over the course of so many lifetimes and find completion.

As I walked, I thought about life and death. I recalled all the pain I had inflicted, willingly and unwillingly, the murders and violations I had perpetrated, the spiteful spells I had uttered. Along came all the memories of how I had suffered, be it at the hands of those who had planted a knife in my throat, those who had cursed me, and all the worse things I had endured since that day when I blissfully officiated as the Oracle of our Mother Earth in an ancient land more than two thousand years earlier. All of it flickered through my mind at the speed of light. With each image, a deep tremor shook my entire system, as if the physical memories held by my body were simultaneously being activated and released.

I realized these were burdens I no longer needed to carry. The time had come to let them go. Each of my steps became a prayer of forgiveness. I forgave those who had done me harm and wished me to hell. And I asked for forgiveness for all the things I had said and done in my ignorance, my hatred and blind resentment. And most of all, I forgave myself for all the pain I had caused myself, for having lost my path and meandered through the darkness for so many centuries. I was ready to once again behold the magnificence of my divine essence, and let its shining light melt away anything unlike itself that still lingered in the shadows of my mind.

In the depth of the night, I arrived at the ruins. There was no moon and the sky was adorned with crisp stars twinkling through the icy cold of the vast plains. The Southern Cross magnificently parted the sky, right above the extensive temple grounds. A small group of men and women sat around a fire, most of them dressed in ceremonial clothing. They welcomed me in my native language and invited me to join them. I walked up the few steps leading into the main precinct and stopped before the eerie silhouettes of the ancient monoliths stoically holding on to their secrets, defying the passing of time. I marveled at the mysterious gate of the sun, a chiseled stone arch dancing in the glow of the crackling flames. It seemingly invited us to step into another dimension and leave behind all limitations imposed by our delusional minds.

More and more people kept coming throughout the night, drawn by a mysterious pull they could neither explain nor understand. They had simply followed their bodies, gathering around our fire with the unspoken faith of those who know they are about to witness something spectacular. I did not see them, but felt the growing human presence around me, and the bubbling energy of joint anticipation. My eyes were closed. As the fire slowly burned to the ground, I sat absorbed by the process of my purification from the past, shedding layer after layer of confusion, being led effortlessly into the deep dark void of pure creative potential. There, surrendered to the longest and blackest of nights, in the silent circle of our prayers, we waited. We waited for the return of the light.

Time stopped. There was no movement, no breath, no sign of life. Only the intense cold and the mute indifference of the stones mocking our impatience in the face of eternity. We held the void with all our courage, willing to hold it forever, trusting life to spring forth once again from the creative miracle of our minds. Slowly, bowing before the pureness of our faith, the stars gently vanished one by one. And then, the first tinge of light appeared on the horizon making our hearts leap with joy.

A play of colors followed, ravishing our senses, preparing the stage for what was yet to come. As the blues and greens gave way to a soft pink hue, we knew doubt was no longer possible. The light was almost upon us. Instinctively, like a tribe from another time, we huddled closer and closer to the giant stone arch, waiting for the first touch of the sun. And suddenly, a single ray born on the horizon pierced through the veil of illusions, falling precisely upon the one that had been waiting motionless since the beginning of time. Irresistibly drawn, we lay our hands upon the stone bathed in gold, and communed with the magnetic light of all-pervading consciousness.

I dissolved in the sun of my rebirth to myself, yielding to the glory of everlasting life. And there, in the infinite intensity of bliss, I felt his presence. There was no doubt possible. I raised my eyes and saw a man looking at me. I was taken back to the day I had spoken as the Oracle and felt his energy matching mine. It was most unexpected, most beautiful. In finding myself again, I had found him. We smiled at each other, and he came towards me through the crowd. He took my hands and stared into my eyes for a long time.

"High Priestess," he said, breaking the silence and playfully bowing before me. "What is your name in this incarnation?"

"Saywa," I answered gently.

"Ahhh!" he said, "The One Who Shows The Way... I see you have landed a name that truly suits you. You are and always shall be our guide."

"And you, dear Sage of countless eons?"

"Well," he smiled mischievously, "that's a good name. Better than any other that has come to pass."

We laughed and laughed, falling into each other's arms, rejoicing at the beauty of human life. How I had unknowingly longed for this moment. How many lifetimes had we passed each other, playing different roles, perhaps never consciously recognizing each other, yet always connected, always together? But now we were whole; we were free from our confusion. And that made all the difference.

X

The Last Words of the Oracle

Maya

I had slept for a long time. I felt groggy, having difficulty pulling myself into wakefulness, swimming through fragments of dreams vanishing into darkness. The sun was out, high in the sky. I walked up to the fire pit, but there was nobody there. I sat down, taking in the view, slightly concerned about my physical state. It had improved, but I was still very weak. After the deep insights and intensity of the previous days, I suddenly found myself exhausted. It was unrealistic to expect that I would miraculously heal within a week of arriving in this country, let alone sustain the bliss I had touched the previous afternoon. And yet, I was disappointed.

A wave of sadness came over me and I wondered whether I would ever make it back to physical health and wellbeing. Would I really be able to change my mind, getting closer and closer to what the Sage had called a state of exclusivity of thinking? And would that really change everything else? As I doubted, I recognized in that doubt the very pattern that I wanted to change, the belief that I was not good enough. Not good enough to be loved. Not good enough to be capable to live up to the Sage's teachings. Not powerful enough to tap into the wisdom necessary to heal myself. I was seeing the very workings of my belief system, and how it could sabotage the change process itself. I thought about the story the Sage had shared the previous afternoon. The path seemed very arduous indeed, if not impossible.

I heard their voices in the distance, chatting happily, laughing. As they appeared, I saw that Magdalena was carrying a cup of steaming tea for me. I felt infinitely blessed to be among such caring souls, but I was so open and vulnerable that I couldn't look at them. Their kindness brought tears to my eyes.

Magdalena sat down next to me and put her arm around me, "You are on the right path," she said. "Lean into the vulnerability. It is there that change can happen. It is there you will find your strength. We always try to push away the discomfort, the doubt, and ignore whatever causes our pain, be it physical or emotional, hoping it will just go away. But part of our journey is to lean into the discomfort for that is where we can find our freedom. That is where we find the connection we have lost, the connection to our higher self, the one who knows all and is all. It is all there. Keep feeling whatever arises. And feel it fully. Eventually, you will become stronger and firmly anchored in the inexhaustible ever-evolving source of life."

I looked up at her and sighed, "Why does it have to be so hard? Why am I so sick?"

And she answered, "You will get better. And seen from a different angle, you can be grateful to your body, for it is thanks to it that you have taken the time to step out of your busy schedule and ask yourself who you are and what life you really want to live. Our body is our most wonderful tool in this life form that we are blessed to experience. Our body speaks with us every moment. It is up to us to learn to listen and follow its guidance and deep wisdom. Every physical sensation is a message. Every emotion has a physical expression. When we do not pay attention, the intensity is increased until we have no other choice, but to listen. Disease is simply our body's attempt to draw our attention when all else has failed. But once we start giving it our awareness, transformation becomes inevitable."

"Come," she said, taking my hand and helping me up, "I want to show you something."

She led me past the entrance to my cave along the base of the rocky cliffs. The trail narrowed and eventually vanished, as the slope below us became rockier and steeper. Magdalena continued slowly, carefully finding footholds in the cracks and crevices, until she came to a halt at what seemed the mouth of a cave. We were probably mid-way between the hilltop and the lake. I stopped to catch my breath, leaning against the rock, and in that instant a condor flew right past us, the wind singing in its majestic wings. Time stopped. I felt the sensation of the wind through its feathers. I saw the precipice from above, as if I was suspended in mid-air. It was beautiful. For a fraction of a second, my soul entered the bird to experience the world through its eyes.

Magdalena laughed. "Now you're starting to understand!" she said, and with that, she turned and walked into the cave. I followed her, my heart beating fast, feeling my way through a narrow corridor, just high enough to stand up straight. The rock felt cool under my hands. We progressed slowly, in silence, letting our eyes adjust to the darkness. After a few minutes, I started hearing the sound of flowing water, and suddenly, the corridor opened up, and we stood in the light of a torch, in a huge dome-shaped cave, very similar in proportions to the one I was sleeping in, but much bigger. It was the cave I had seen in the Sage's story.

Two torches were burning, on either side. The roof above them was blackened, but there was no smoke. The air was fresh and as we kept walking further in, towards the back of the cave, the sound of water became louder and louder. We arrived at a river, rushing out of the rocks in a beautiful transparent cascade, only to disappear a few meters further in the ground. There was an opening in the wall behind the cascade, a corridor disappearing into the darkness.

"If we follow this channel, we get to the lake," she said. "But for today, we will stay here. This is a very special place. It has been used for many purposes over the years. During the times of our people's great struggle, it was a place of shelter and hiding. But long before that, in ancient times, it was a site used for ritual and divination. In the company of a shaman, the initiate could enter the cave and behold the visions necessary for her healing and spiritual evolution. I have come here many times, in different pasts, as different versions of myself. Now, if you wish, you may go deeper, and receive the gifts that lie in waiting. Are you ready?"

"Yes," I answered, humbled by the awe-inspiring surroundings. I was ready. The Sage had said: 'There is more. There is always more,' and I was curious. My first insight into the underworld of my mind was still alive within me. I could barely embrace the beauty of the experience of love that had traversed me, and the clear answers I had received to the question: Who am I? Likewise, I was still shaken by the deeply engrained beliefs that had played their part in creating the circumstances of my life.

I wanted to know more.

Magdalena spread out some blankets in the center of the cave, between the two torches and invited me to lie down and close my eyes. "Simply be present to the sensations in your body. You don't need to do anything. Just start by feeling the sensations and witness what unfolds. You might see or hear things. Let your mind rest and be present to whatever arises, without judgment and without taking control of what is unfolding. If you need me, I am here, right next to you. I will watch over you, so that you may enter the dream-world in full serenity, welcoming the healing that wants to take place."

I lay down, closed my eyes, and concentrated on the physical sensations in my body. Very quickly, my whole being started vibrating, as if each cell was tuning into a sacred energy flow that seemed to permeate the cave. I focused my awareness on this subtle vibration, dropping deeper and deeper. And then, the images came. I was transported into another time, another place. Another reality.

It is dark. The full moon has already set behind the hills and dawn has yet to break. I am in a small stone house, sharing the single room with a man who is my father and my three siblings. I feel a calling, an urge to get up and go to the sanctuary. It is not time yet, but I am starting to learn to listen to my inner voice. I close my eyes once more and hear Her loud and clear, "Come to me now," She calls.

I get dressed as silently as possible and step out into the intense darkness that precedes dawn, closing the squeaking wooden door behind me. I run up the trail towards the sanctuary. All is silent. Even the sheep dogs are asleep. On the last curve, I slow down to catch my breath. As I enter the temple grounds, my whole body tenses up and a wave of sadness hits me. I stop breathing as a wave of premonition floods in. No, it can't be. It can't be. Overwhelmed by panic, I ask the unthinkable, "She's gone, isn't she?"

"Yes," comes the answer.

I start shaking. I am frozen with fear, feeling lost and abandoned. She has been the mother that I never knew, and now she too is gone. I am not ready for this. I still need her. Why did she go now? She who knew all and felt all things, why did she choose to leave? What will happen to me now? Again come the words, urging me to walk on, "Come to me now!"

And so, I go. I go to the rock and sit on the ground, leaning against it, weeping inconsolably. Suddenly, amidst my tears, I hear her voice. Not the voice of Gaia, the one she taught me to connect with through my months of training, but the voice of the Priestess, my beloved teacher. I raise my eyes and she is there, standing before me in the grass, in a soft glowing light, majestically draped in her white robes. She looks at me lovingly.

"My time in Her service has come to an end," she says. "This may seem hard to you, but sometimes, there is a higher order to things, which we cannot grasp from our limited human perspective. We can only accept that our understanding is incomplete and pray for the great wisdom that will open our eyes. Your training is not finished, but you have progressed enough that I may continue the teachings from the other side.

"I was much younger than you when my teacher left her body. You may not think so, but you are ready for that which is to come. Even though you will no longer see me as you do now, I will always be available to you. Whenever you need me, I will come. You will feel my presence. As long as you keep yourself open and in permanent connection with the deep wisdom of the Great Mother, all that you need to know will come to you. Only fear can obstruct the channel. No matter what happens, do not let fear cloud your mind."

The vision before me dissolves. Dawn pierces the darkness and the sky drapes itself in beautiful colors. Dogs bark in the distance. The Earth feels warm under my feet. I can still feel her presence exactly as she has foretold, and it reassures me. Perhaps she has not left me after all. Perhaps I am to learn to experience life in a different way, beyond the physical, into the felt truth that is becoming a growing reality inside of me.

As I calm myself down, prepared for what is to come, I hear her speak to me as if she was still standing there, "Soon you will be ready to become the Oracle and speak by Her grace. From now on, you will sleep in the sanctuary, in the cave at the back that serves as the abode of the Priestess. But today, stay where you are. Do not speak to anybody. Simply stay by the rock, feel the energy around and within, feel into your new role and wait for night to come."

I sit in meditation by the rock. She is still with me and I feel protected. The day seems like any other: birds gaily welcoming the sun, the first workers walking up the trail to continue the strenuous construction of the temple. The air is heating up rapidly. But as the hours pass, the most attuned among the women who care for the sanctuary start picking up the disturbance in the field, noticing her absence. It is not yet a reason to worry, as she usually welcomed dawn on her own, high up on the mountain, overlooking the valley. She sometimes only returned shortly before noon, with the intense heat, and met me under the olive trees next to her cave at the base of the cliffs. But today, no one comes down from the mountain. I sit in the shade of the rock, eyes closed, and feel the rising agitation around me. The rumors start spreading. By late afternoon, some of the shepherds from the village hike up into the mountains to look for her. I take it all in from where I am sitting. I am hungry and in pain. But I don't move. I wait for further guidance.

Night comes. The shepherds return from their search, promising to continue the next day. All go to their homes, and I, alone, remain where I am. No one comes to bother me. They know that the young Priestess in training receives specific instructions in the course of her initiation, sometimes involving prolonged periods of fasting and meditation. It is not for anyone to question.

Everything is silent. The sky is sprinkled with stars, waiting for the moon to come out and eclipse their brightness. The air is getting cooler, the wind picking up in intensity. I sit and wait, and whenever hints of anxiety rise to the surface of my mind, I replay her words, until the exhaustion catches up with me and I fall asleep on the bare earth, inhaling the vapors in my sleep.

I have vivid dreams: images of a finished temple, in the heart of which lies a dark chamber where the Oracle shrieks incomprehensible sounds as she writhes her hands and rolls her eyes. She has no direct contact with the men and women laden with riches who have come to seek her wisdom. The priests are the intermediaries. They interpret and deliver her words. Sometimes, within days of uttering the prophecy in a hysterical state, she succumbs, and another priestess is chosen to take her place. In a semi-lucid state, bewildered, I watch the stream of images flowing before my eyes: the temple complex growing in size and wealth, hundreds of powerful visitors coming from faraway lands, the men who control the questions that come in and the prophecies that go out, and the young priestesses who succeed one another. I see these women, devoted and pure, and yet, their devotion is no longer to Gaia. It is to another form, another shape that has cloaked the grace of the One to whom I have given my life.

I wake up in sweat, my heart beating fast, wondering what all this means. And I hear Her speak to me, "What you have seen is one version of the future in manifest. The collective thoughts and choices of those who are here will determine the future of this sanctuary. It will serve as a metaphor for the world, a metaphor for the human mind, and its ripple effects will be felt for millennia. You were born to serve as an actor and witness to this transformation. Your journey is not an easy one. Yet, I ask you to serve as my Oracle. You may be the last Priestess of Gaia officiating in this sanctuary for a long time to come. It will take all you know. But do not fear. You will be guided."

I fall asleep again, holding tightly to these words, engraving them on my heart and mind. I wake at dawn, deeply shaken by my dreams and by all I have seen and heard since leaving my father's house the previous morning. I swiftly retreat to what used to be my teacher's abode. They continue the search for many days, but she is nowhere to be found. And those who see me walk to the cave that morning understand that she will not come back. They know I have been instructed to take her place.

The man who was her lover has disappeared as well, along with his boat. Someone spotted it on the horizon on the morning she was found missing. Rumors spread that they escaped together, that she relinquished her divine calling for a man. This story quickly becomes the accepted version of the truth, and people spare no judgment on her behalf, using her example as evidence that carnal love is incompatible with the duties and purity required of a Priestess of Gaia.

I know that she has been killed, and that she did not fight the impending death coming towards her. And I suspect that he risked a similar fate but managed to escape. I know but I cannot speak the truth, for no one asks. And thus I learn that truth is a matter of choice. That men are afraid of the power of a woman deeply anchored in the source of all knowledge, a woman who embodies the timeless wisdom and great mysteries of Life itself. They can admire her from afar as long as she stays confined within strict boundaries that do not threaten their beliefs about themselves. But as soon as she steps across and tears asunder all limitations imposed by the mind, she becomes a menace, projecting back at them the image of the shackles they are dragging through their existence. Getting rid of her is less frightening than unlocking their own chains.

In my mind, the thought forms that being a woman is a threat. A threat to others. A threat to yourself. I feel trapped. My teacher prepared me to be a pure channel, immensely powerful, seeing through the apparent and into the deeper dimensions of existence. She prepared me to be free, to move beyond ordinary self-imposed limitations. She taught me to have complete faith in the infinite potential of the human soul and the divine power that graces the ones devoted to serving Life. And yet, these very attributes now seem to place my life in danger. If I shine in the full glory for which I am destined, will they choose to eliminate me as well? And I call up Her words, "Do not fear. You will be guided," to create a shield keeping at bay the fear lurking in the dark corners of my soul.

Months pass as I battle with my inner questions and doubts. The works continue and even though they are not complete yet, word has spread that the Oracle will soon start speaking the truth from within the splendor of the new temple of the Sun God, a tribute to His all-illuminating powers. The first visitors arrive with questions and offerings, and the rulers of the temple decide to reinstate the monthly oracular revelations. It is time for me to step into my role.

But how can I? For me, it is a time of great struggle and confusion. I have been taught to open myself to Her grace and infinite wisdom. I am attuned to the Earth and her seasons, to the magic of the moon, the ebb and flow of the tide as it recounts the story of human life and death. Yet, those who come are devotees of a God that embodies a different quality of human experience. They are looking for the power and constancy of the shining sun; they seek to build their foundations on that which lies revealed in its eternal light. They want to forcefully banish the darkness and subdue the wisdom that squirms in the shadows.

How can I speak for them? I who am speaking from the darkness, I who am feeling into the deep black wells of the elusive, using my entire being to catch the fleeting silvery scales of truth sliding past. They want the light of the sun. I can give them the unpredictable slimy substance of the shadow. And that changes everything.

There are external changes too. In the absence of the formidable presence and all-penetrating gaze of the Priestess, the newcomers are slowly taking control of the sanctuary, their authority seeping from construction decisions into how the ceremonies are to be conducted. I am still hesitant in my role, lacking the strength and confidence to assert my power against them. I feel a widening gap between my inner devotion to the Goddess and what I see emerging day after day on our temple grounds. I remember the visions in my dreams and wonder whether our collective fate has already been sealed.

I seek counsel from my teacher, calling her in my meditation. She encourages me to prepare according to the tradition, ignoring the apparent outer transformations and expectations. I follow her instructions. Seven days after the new moon, the new date chosen for the revelations, I am ready. They have carved a chamber in the bedrock, right behind the original site, along the primordial chasm that extends deep into the ground. The temple is being built around this chamber, upwards towards the sky. Columns have been erected, and the imposing stone slabs through which the supplicants will enter to the north-east are in place. Only the roof is missing.

At dawn, I walk towards the temple. I feel the presence of many men and women waiting on these sacred grounds, eager to be led upwards, hungry for the words of the Oracle. I am nervous. I feel exposed and unsure of my capacity to speak publicly the answers that will be given to me. I enter and slowly walk down the narrow staircase into the dark chamber. It is intimidating at first, but soon I feel that I am walking towards the heart of the Earth. I am suddenly permeated by Her awesome energy and feel reassured. I sit down on the three-legged stool that has been placed over the fissure in the darkest depths. And I wait.

A scribe comes down and sits at the base of the stairs. He has been instructed to write down every word I utter. In the past, the Oracle spoke in front of all those who wished to hear, and the words were received with the energetic intensity with which they were spoken. Now the words of the Oracle will only be audible to those in the chamber, and the newly-appointed priests officiating in the temple above. Her words will be captured, rendered frozen and inert, subject to multiple interpretations by those who were not present to receive that which happens beyond the spoken word.

I am no longer in control of the external proceedings. The vapors are strong in the chamber, and I can feel their exhilarating effect. I stay intensely focused, feeling connected and blessed to simply be in Her presence. My fear and confusion vanish. The doubts that have plagued me for months evaporate as I admire the play of shadows on the stone walls and the occasional wisps of smoke rising from the depths, obscuring the dim light of the oil lamp by my side.

A man comes down the stairs and kneels at the far end of the chamber, looking at me with great awe and reverence. In the faint daylight coming down the shaft, I notice that he is dressed in elegant clothing, a mark of his status. He has a gentle feel about him. I wonder whether I have seen him before.

"What is your question for the Oracle?" I ask, serenely.

"I have come from afar on behalf of my friend and companion, who cannot make the journey because of his duties," he whispers. "He officiates in the great healing sanctuary beyond the mountains, where the waters meet the land under the morning sun. He had a dream of a young woman dressed in white, coming to him on a ship, fleeing persecution. He took her in with open arms and led her under a tree, where she closed her eyes and spoke the truth. He asks for your wisdom to elucidate his vision."

I see the vision as soon as he starts describing it and gasp, as I understand the hidden message in the man's words. The companion he spoke of is the man who came to our sanctuary to lead the construction of the temple, the man who became my teacher's lover, and who disappeared on the dawn of her death. I see him in a beautiful valley by the sea, where many come to him to seek healing. They stay for weeks, sleeping in the temple, where they are guided to find relief in the symbolic language of their dreams. There is an ancient tree in the shade of which sits an Oracle. As I look, it becomes clear that I am the young woman who crosses the seas to find him. I am the woman sitting under the tree.

His words are not a question; they are a coded message of invitation, an out-stretched hand to help me, should I need it. I am shaking, and for a few seconds do not know how to respond. But then, Her words come through and I give them my voice, "The vision speaks of the power of the feminine forces of intuition. They are at threat of being forlorn, supplanted by other forces, and yet, your friend has found the path to rescue them from impending doom and welcome them into his heart. By opening his arms to his inner wisdom, he is reconnecting to the archaic energy of the Great Mother and finding the truth within. He has completed the circle of coming into wholeness and many will seek his guidance and healing now, and in many futures to come. She, in inner form has come to him. She, in outer form need not come, although she may."

He bows deep before me, adding, "My ship will leave at dusk three days from now to bring back your all-seeing words of wisdom." And with that, he turns and walks back up the steps in silence.

Men and women succeed him, asking about sickness and childbearing, about family disputes and the distribution of wealth, about undertaking long journeys at sea and the ideal site to build a new home. The first visitor deeply troubled me, but I quickly slide back into a deep state of surrender, where the answers to subsequent queries come flowing through me, one after the other. In this state of trance, what is at stake for my own human existence becomes irrelevant; I embody more than my narrow personality. I see clearly through the confusion the potential that lurks within those who stand before me, waiting to be freed, waiting to be brought into awareness. As I sit on my stool, I shine the light into their inner darkness to banish doubt and help them connect more deeply to that which is already there.

It is getting very dark in the chamber. The sun has probably set by now. But I am not tired. The scribe bows and gets up, signaling that the day's ceremonies are over. For some reason, however, I do not get up. It is as if She is asking me to stay, as if there is one more question yet to be answered. And so I wait. Shortly thereafter, steps resound on the platform above and the shadow of a man descends towards me. It is one of the self-appointed priests.

"Priestess," he starts, without a bow or sign of reverence, "the Oracle's counsel is wise and has been gratefully received by all those who came to see you today. But there is one question which remains, voiced by those among us who are eager to spread the all-seeing and all-knowing reputation of the Oracle of our new temple. From whom do you derive your power? Who is the voice that speaks through you? To whom do you pledge your allegiance?"

My lips start moving and the words form without my control, "Do not concern yourself with understanding the source, for the source cannot be known by your intellectual mind. You can only understand it once you become it. Whatever temples you may build, whatever external envelope you may construct, the source remains unchanged. The connection is strong here, because it has been a sanctuary for eons, a place where men and women have brought their love and devotion, thus upholding the vibration that the Earth offers to the ones who connect with Her. But there is no external power. There is no external allegiance. There is only connection. And connection is independent of time and place."

He is shuffling around at the far end of the chamber. This is clearly not the answer he expected. I can feel his discontent. And I continue, "There is only one path that leads to connection with the source and its power: behold the two words that are engraved on the north-eastern lintel of your temple – *Know thyself!*"

There is nothing else to be said and after this last sentence, I remain silent, waiting for him to leave. His steps eventually echo up heavily, and finally all grows quiet. I rise in the flickering light of the oil lamp and slowly walk out into the night. Within minutes of leaving the temple, an immense wave of tiredness hits me. I am exhausted. The words I spoke, the visions I saw, all seem like a blur. I barely manage to reach my cave and lie down.

In the middle of the night, I wake up. I am no longer the Oracle. I am a young woman and I am afraid because I know too much and I have seen what they are capable of. I recall the priest's stern face as he asked me his question. And I remember the invitation to sail away to the valley beyond the mountains, and the Oracle's response, "She, in outer form need not come, although she may." She left it open for me to decide. How strange. What does this mean? I shift around not finding sleep, wondering what to do, wondering whether my life is in danger if I choose to stay. And I hear my teacher's voice, "Only fear can silence the truth. Do not follow the fear path, for you won't like where it leads you."

The very next day, everything starts spiraling downwards rapidly. Just as the first visitor's question was in fact an invitation, the priest's question was a warning, an injunction to tread carefully so as not to upset the new order cementing itself into the foundations of the temple. I think about escaping on the ship, but my mind is clouded by confusion. The right course of action remains unclear. Do I really need to run away?

The sun sets on the third day, and the ship sails away without me. I have convinced myself that my place is in the sanctuary to which I have dedicated my life. She asked me to serve as Her Oracle. Doesn't this mean that I am to stay? I assure myself that this is the right decision, and hope that I will not come to regret letting that opportunity slip through my fingers.

And then, little by little, without being aware of it, I become afraid. Afraid of being watched. Afraid of being followed.

Wherever I go, whatever I do, I check my surroundings, and every so often, seem to notice one of the priests somewhere in the vicinity. When I step out of my cave at dawn, I sometimes spot one of them sitting under a tree, pretending to be absorbed in contemplation. When I go for a walk, I feel that someone is stalking me. When I sit and admire the view, when I pick wild herbs, when I sweep the temple grounds, whatever I do, there always seems to be a presence watching me.

At first, I pretend not to notice their intimidating maneuvers. But fear quickly has the upper hand. And the more I fear them, the more menacing they seem to become. They never say anything to me; they never come close, and on the surface life in the sanctuary seems to continue undisturbed. But beneath the skin, my confidence and serenity are being chipped away, day after day.

All the emotions that surfaced when my teacher died creep back in, permanently planting their flags of conquest in the dark corners of my mind: the feeling that being a woman is a threat, that I am at the mercy of those around me, that I have been abandoned, the feeling that I am not up for the great task before me. I fear my own power. I fear for my life. My dreams, which until now were a source of clarity and deeper understanding become a reflection of my inner travails: dreams of persecution, dreams of being murdered.

I am on guard twenty-four hours a day. I jump at every noise. Every shadow makes my heart beat faster. Little by little, the roots I had grown into the Earth, my connection, the source of my confidence and joy dry up. I don't notice it immediately. But when it hits me, it is too late. Several months have passed. The winter has come and the next Oracular ceremony is planned to coincide with the return of spring. Life has become very still. Shepherds take their sheep to graze in the hills. Villagers tend to their winter crops. For all, the dimmer light and longer nights are a time to keep warm and turn inwards.

I walk up to the top of the cliffs. The winds are strong and it is very cold. I sit down in a sheltered nook in the rocks to admire the view. The sea, usually calm in the bay, is dotted with whitecaps. It is as if nature has unleashed her full fury to remind me of the awesome power that moves beneath me. I remember and I call upon the depths of Her wisdom. But I am faced with a vast desert haunted by doubt. She is silent. And when words eventually form, I no longer know whether they come from Her, or whether they are made up by my imagination in a desperate attempt to prove to myself that I can still receive Her. The more I try, the more I slip into the thickness of my confusion. Until I stop trying, coming face to face with the shocking truth: I have lost my connection. I have lost my inner light.

As I walk back down to the sanctuary, I mourn the end of my life as the Oracle. In the days that follow, I can barely function, paralyzed by the shame of my defeat, and the fear of what might happen if anyone finds out. I can no longer hear Her, nor my teacher, yet here I am, walking around the temple grounds dressed in white robes. I feel like an imposter. I daydream of escape, of sailing away to the valley beyond the mountains across the sea. But how could I? He was ready to welcome an Oracle; yet all trace of that wise woman is gone from within me. I can barely look at my own shadow. I have to leave; there is no question about it. But where will I go?

Shortly thereafter, I receive a message from my eldest brother, asking me to come and bless his newborn girl. As I walk over to the village, one of the priests accompanies me, but dares not enter the house. I openly share my fears with my brother, and my desire to leave. He can scarcely understand my pleas. As the Oracle, I am shrouded in an aura of supernatural powers. Expressions of human emotions such as fear and doubt are not expected of an initiate who is thought to have stepped into a reality free from human concerns. Nevertheless, faced with the sincere urgency of my distress, he accepts to help me. He gives me a bundle of clothes to dress as a shepherd, and we agree upon a time and place where he will meet me and accompany me to the next village, from whence he will arrange for a cousin to lead me further into the mountains.

On the appointed night, a storm is raging, providing the perfect setting for me to slip away unnoticed through the shadows of swaying trees and the howling wind echoing my inner despair at my ultimate defeat. My brother is there, as agreed, his slender frame barely perceptible in the fog of the low hanging clouds. We walk in silence through the gusts and the pouring rain, through the cold of the night. When we reach my cousin's house, I feel relieved. No one followed us. No one is watching me. I am free again, free from the menacing gaze of the priests, free from expectations, and playing a role I have become estranged from, free from being the one whom others look to for answers. I decide to erase the past and start a new life.

Many years have passed. I am an old woman now, sitting on the side of a mountain. Two little girls are playing with a kitten by my side. They are my grandchildren. I have never seen their faces, because I am blind. But I love to sit and listen to the wind gently rustling through the trees, the children's laughter, the bells of the sheep and goats grazing nearby, the crashing waves of the sea rolling in the distance. My past was buried a long time ago, but now that I know that my life will soon come to an end, I wonder what would have happened if I had sailed away on that ship. I like to think that I am at peace, that I am ready to go. Yet beneath the surface lies a deep lake of melancholy, in whose waters shimmers a potential unfulfilled, a connection forlorn, a past glory forsaken.

XI

Trapped on the Fear Path

Maya

We had walked back from the big cave in silence. Clouds had come in over the mountains, and a lightning storm was brewing over the distant snow-capped peaks. I felt dizzy, stunned by my new discovery, amazed at the clarity of the vision I had just experienced. In my first session with the Sage, I had experienced myself as a newborn baby, a small child, and then as an unlimited energy form, abstract yet very tangible. In the cave, however, a whole new dimension had opened up as I experienced the full life of the little girl who became the Oracle, all her thoughts and fears down to the very last detail. There was no doubt possible. It had not been a dream. It was truly as if I had lived that life, impossible to conceive of as purely a product of my imagination. Was I somehow connecting to the collective consciousness of humanity, absorbing as my own an experience lived by someone else? It didn't feel like she had been someone else; she had shared so many of my personality traits and emotions. And beyond the obvious difference in external circumstances, there were many eerie parallels with my current life. Could it really be that we lived many lives?

The Sage appeared on the trail, pulling me from my musings with his deep smile and playful sparkling eyes. He handed me a big plate of food. "Here," he said. "You may want to rest for a while; our journeys into the past are more tiring than we may think. As soon as you're ready, come join us at the top of the hill, so that we may talk about what you have just experienced."

We sat in the grass on the hilltop. The sky was dark, but it was still warm. I had slept for more than an hour, a very deep dreamless sleep, and felt as if I was in a world between worlds. I was not quite sure what to say or where to start. But once again, the Sage spoke as if he had been in my mind the whole time, feeling every single thing I had seen, almost with more precision than I myself had experienced it.

"Remember the words you were given two days ago: '*You are Energy refining itself. You are Love experiencing itself. You are Life becoming more.*' You are energy! And energy never dies, it simply changes form. You are a vibrational frequency coming into cohesion, into a state of pure perfection. A state where there is no interference from any contradictory energies, any thoughts of separation or limitation. In other words, at your essence, you are Love: a vibrational state of absolute creativity.

"And so, what if you really did live many lifetimes? What if on your journey of refining or streamlining your energy, uncluttering it from what you are not, you were given the opportunity to come and go over lifetimes, to experience and resolve, eventually evolving towards what I referred to yesterday as exclusivity of thinking? And in doing so, what if you were able to move from confusion to clarity, from fragmentation to cohesion, until the energy that you are reaches its ultimate vibrational frequency: a state of pure creative potential?

"This idea of living dozens, hundreds or perhaps even more lives may seem strange to you. Perhaps even more so, if I suggested that they do not succeed one another linearly, but that you are living all of them at the same time, in a multi-dimensional universe, the comprehension of which is beyond our limited vantage point. What you think about all this is actually not that important; your visions do not even need to be taken literally. Just know that whatever comes up is meant to help you further your understanding of yourself and aid in the transformation constantly wanting to take place right here and right now. Whenever we open up our awareness, our mind automatically delivers to us whatever we need for our evolution. It may be in the form of a physical sensation, an insight, a vision, or what could be interpreted as an experience of a past life.

"There are certain themes that we work on again and again, and we work on them over what seems to be lifetimes. They are all variations of what you saw on your first journey in trance, namely our misguided beliefs about ourselves, about who and what we really are, about why we are here. In the process of our spiritual evolution, we work on these themes by playing with different scenarios that give us the opportunity to fully experience, become aware of, and transcend our self-imposed limitations.

"In the story of your current life that you shared with us on the first night, and in your life as the Priestess of Gaia, there is an important recurrent theme." He paused, smiling, looking at Magdalena with what seemed utter devotion.

She picked up from him, "Yes indeed... the mother of all themes: reclaiming the feminine. It is an important theme for all of us, women and men, and for the world: coming into balance. It is about reclaiming our intuition, the voice that speaks in the dark. About reconnecting with the one who reveals herself in the moonlight, in the whispers of dead leaves crackling under our feet. She, the impermanent One, shining in the eyes of a newborn child and in the creases of an old man's hands. She, the force of change. Powerful beyond measure. Forever untamed. We must accept her in the fullness of her glory, fierce and gentle, soft and wild. Only thus will we be showered with the grace of Her presence. And to do that, we must start by remembering that we are also made of flesh and bone, that we have the capacity to know by feeling, to know through this amazing body of ours."

She bowed to the earth and to the sky, to the lake and the distant peaks, and sat down by my side, taking me in her arms. In the earthiness of her touch, I felt the forces of nature flowing through me. Her fearlessness. Her awesome power. Her gentleness.

The Sage continued, "In your life as Maya, you have been torn between two worlds. A world that glorified the rational qualities of your mind, your capacity to think far and deep, provide structure and analyze, break everything down into pieces to be observed and understood through logical thinking. And a world of intuition and magic, feeling and instant knowledge coming through your body. You embraced the former and repressed the latter, believing that in doing so, you would gain the approval of those around you and walk the sunlit trail of human development.

"Your desire to be loved and your fear of abandonment led you to behave according to the wishes of those you loved. And they, believing they were acting in your best interest, called you out of the wild forests, and out of the graveyard, into the austere wooden desolation of the church, and later, into the dry institutions of the intellect. Don't get me wrong: cultivation of the intellect and its amazing potential is as important as reconnecting with the source. The problem lies in the belief that they are antagonistic, that one can only be developed at the expense of the other; the belief that thinking and control take precedence over feeling and flowing, intelligence over intuition. Both need to be nurtured equally and integrated for our coming into wholeness. This is the significance of the dream-vision-invitation from the distant valley that you aptly decoded when you first spoke as the Oracle."

As the Sage spoke, I remembered an incident that I had long forgotten. I was about fifteen at the time, and I attended the church youth meetings that took place under the guidance of my father. We usually read a passage from the Bible and discussed its direct relevance to our lives. We were a lively group and the exchanges were always quite interesting. One day, however, my father opened up the meeting with a grave voice, "Today, before we turn to our weekly reading, I want to raise an important topic. I would like our young brother here to share with you the question he asked me after our Sunday service."

One of the younger members of our group, stepped forward, and with a slightly intimidated look, complied with the priest's invitation, "I asked if it was normal to hear voices in one's head. I asked whether they were angels or whether God could speak to us directly."

My father thanked him, motioning him back to his chair. Then he said, "Now, if you had been in one of our sister churches, they might have told you that you are hearing angels or some other such nonsense. With a bit less luck, they would have tried to exorcise you, seeing in these voices the work of the devil, which they believe needs to be extracted from your being by having a bunch of people screaming at you. In this church, however, let it be very clear that there is only one fundament to our faith: our intellect. Our God-given, unparalleled, most brilliant faculty to reason; that which enables us to see magic and all other absurd fallacies of our imagination for what they are: pure superstition."

I saw the boy shrinking in his chair, blushing at the neck, trying to conceal his shame. It was awful. I wanted to say something to the extent that the Bible was full of angels and people who heard the voice of God. Why wouldn't we? But my father's mere presence was so crushing that I remained silent, lowered my head and waited to see which text we would now have the pleasure of dissecting under the austere light of this church in which every inkling of juicy life had been dried out, lest it stir the unpalatable emotions hiding in our shadows.

"Yes," the Sage nodded sympathetically, "if you think about your life and experiences like this one, you will understand better the intensity of your inner conflict. You will see how the growing imbalance that you experienced between your suppressed intuitive self and your deified intellect, resulted at last in disease. Your body eventually collapsed, begging you to listen to its wisdom and reconnect with its teachings. In the vision you had in the cave, this theme of suppression of the feminine played out in a different way for you to see and understand the roots of this pattern more deeply.

"Your life as the Priestess is highly insightful because the Oracle represents the ultimate metaphor for the embodied feminine. The Oracle is the one who can connect with Gaia, the Mother Earth, source of all life. She is the Priestess who is able to receive and speak Her words. She is fully devoted to the feminine from a young age and trained to surrender to Her infinite power and wisdom, putting her individual life at the service of the whole, as she learns to see through Her eyes and transcend her limited being by merging with that which is unlimited.

"This is who you were. This is how deeply you walked that path. You were chosen to be an embodiment of the divine feminine, because that potential lay within you. And it still does to this very day. The question is: Was that potential fulfilled, then and now? And if not, what happened?"

I recalled the vision of me as the old woman sitting on the mountain. The seer who had become blind. My nostalgia and underlying pain at the latent greatness that had slipped through my fingers. And I thought about my current life and the desperate state I found myself in. I had not lived to my full potential. Neither then, nor now. What had happened? Then, it had all started with the shock I experienced with the death of my teacher, the great Priestess. From that moment on, despite her warning, I had started living under the grip of fear.

And the Sage said, "Remember that events are neutral in themselves; it is our interpretation that determines the impact they will have in our lives. The death of your teacher triggered something very deep within you. Then, as now, your birth mother had left you at an early age, gnawing away at your feeling of self-worth, subconsciously raising the question again and again of whether you deserved to be loved, and whether you were worthy of the highly admired function of Priestess of Gaia. Nevertheless, at first, you still felt the presence of your teacher because you were anchored in Life, able to connect with and speak the wisdom of the Great Mother, able to feel beyond the illusion and understand that it is simply not possible to be abandoned, because there is no separation.

"But your roots were fragile. And your fear was being kindled by the external circumstances, sending you the message that being a woman was dangerous, that you knew too much, that you were too powerful, that it was safer to play small. Yet, playing small was not compatible with your role as the Oracle. You were stuck in this seemingly insoluble dilemma. Meanwhile, the priests slowly took over, supplanting Gaia with their God, exposing their hidden intentions to silence the all-powerful Oracle by becoming the interpreters of Her truth. This story is a metaphor for the mind and for the world, the masculine overthrowing the feminine, the intellect analyzing and interpreting the revealed intuitive truth, distorting the reality that simply is by needing it to be explained and understood. You unknowingly internalized these external threats and silenced yourself through your fear of your own power."

"Is that what she meant, when she said: Do not follow the fear path, for you won't like where it leads you?" I asked.

"Exactly," he answered. "You were guided very strongly then, as you are now. You were given the opportunity to experience fear in many dimensions, and see how it can destroy everything it attaches itself to. You see, our predominant emotion dictates our behavior. In other words, when we are afraid, we direct energy towards the object of our fear. As we try to repress our fear, we only give more energy to that which we try to avoid. The more energy we give it, the more it expands in our lives, until it becomes a reality. You were afraid of your own power, and thus you destroyed that very power by suppressing it within you. You were afraid that the priests might kill you, and thus you ended up killing your Oracle-self. You thought that being a woman was a threat, and thus you crushed the feminine force alive within you, losing not only your ability to hear, but also to see.

"There is another important element. As you spoke for the first – and last – time as the Oracle, you were at an important fork in the road. Just as in the story I shared yesterday, you stood on your own version of the juncture on the path. Your fears were alive and busy creating your future, yet you were still anchored deeply in the Great Mother and able to hear Her guidance. It was a critical moment. The danger latent in the external circumstances was becoming clear and potentially insurmountable. Yet, that same day you received a message, which you correctly recognized as an invitation. You received no specific instruction regarding the path to follow: your fate lay in your hands. But you chose to dismiss the invitation and continue down the path of fear.

"I have already mentioned how important it is, in moments of great struggle, to slow down and become fully aware of what we say 'yes' to, and what we say 'no' to. We have to become aware of the underlying forces that condition each and every one of our choices. In this case, perhaps you underestimated the broader setting closing in on you and the detrimental impact of your fear as it spiraled out of control. Nor did you see how serendipitous it was that the very man, whom you spoke of as having integrated the divine feminine to achieve wholeness, offered you the opportunity to continue honoring your calling by becoming the Oracle on his land. You were confused, the three days came and went, the ship sailed away, and by not saying yes, in effect, you were saying no.

"Now, as then, you are at a fork in the road. You heard your body's call. You heard the voice of Gaia and opened your inner vision such that you were able to see Magdalena come visit you in your apartment in the city, and understand her coded message of invitation."

Startled, I turned to Magdalena sitting by my side, "Do you mean to say that you didn't actually come to my apartment?" I whispered.

"Reality is not what you think it is," she answered. "Presence does not know the boundaries of time and space. The deeper we go, the less we are subject to commonly agreed upon physical laws. I still see the Priestess in you. You have a profound capacity to see. And thus, when I heard your call for help, I came. I knew you would see me, just as you had seen me then, shortly after my death in the sanctuary."

I was astounded. Everything suddenly made sense. Life was incredible beyond belief. It was too perfect to be possible. I marveled at the profundity of all I had lived, then and now. I looked at her with big open eyes, as if I was seeing her for the first time, as if I had found my family after centuries of searching. She was my teacher not only in this life, but in others too. Our paths had crossed again and again.

They couldn't help but laugh at my dumbfounded loving gaze, as I stuttered, "So... Life keeps repeating itself?"

"Yes," the Sage said. "It often does, so that we may work on the same theme from different angles, exploring all its facets. We keep going around the circle until we learn enough to move to another theme, another layer. This time around, you seized the invitation. You came. And now you have an opportunity to look at your mind deeply, analyzing and feeling, understanding and seeing, engaging with life in a new way. For you, this is an opportunity for completion. A time to rewrite your story in full consciousness, to change your future by resolving your past."

"What do you mean by 'resolving my past'?" I asked. "Isn't it enough to focus on consciously manifesting the future that I really want?"

"Tomorrow, I will show you," he smiled. "It has been a long day. Let us sit and enjoy the mystical light of dusk."

XII

Resolving the Past

Maya

I was feeling much better. For the first time since I arrived on the island, I had risen before dawn. As I squeezed out of my cave into the fading darkness, I saw a steaming cup of tea awaiting me on the small grassy platform outside; an invitation to sit and relish the play of lights. On this island it seemed that manifestation was instantaneous. One only needed to awaken with a longing for hot tea, and there it appeared. And not any kind of tea: a careful concoction of healing herbs from the island. I had to laugh. Could life really be as simple as it seemed when living in the presence of a Sage and a Priestess?

As I sat there awaiting dawn in a state of childish wonder, I suddenly didn't know where I was anymore. Which time period was this, which reality, which version of myself? All these faces, all these stories, all these beliefs. Was I the Oracle of times past, tending to the inner doubts of countless seekers? Was I the lucid alcoholic from the Sage's story drowning in my inability to let go of my beliefs of unworthiness? Was I the little girl standing before the Genie, asking to be given nothing? Was I a deeply sensitive indigenous girl adopted by a stern priest? Or was I an over-achieving woman looking into the workings of my mind in an attempt to heal myself?

"You are energy refining itself, playing with the illusion of limitation."

The voice had come from within. She was speaking. She was there. The connection was back. What a relief.

I smiled, rejoicing, and walked up to the clearing.

"Good morning!" The Sage was facing the sun, arms raised in salutation to a glorious new day. "As you saw this morning," he added, amused, "you manifest very fast. It is a testament to how far you have come and to the tremendous power awakening in you. Be very aware of your thoughts though, because when we become capable of almost instantly manifesting what we might consider desirable events and circumstances, the same goes for their opposites. It is a strong reminder to watch where your mind goes, for the further you walk on this journey towards oneness, the more you will instantly experience your thoughts, whatever they may be. Anything you can think, you can experience. There are no limits.

"And that brings us to your question about manifesting our future and resolving our past. As I mentioned yesterday, we attract to us that which reflects our beliefs. Consciously manifesting our future means vibrating at the frequency of that which we want to attract. Practically, we may find it useful to envision the future we would like in great detail, in all its dimensions. We can even resort to literally writing the script of our life as an aid to crystalizing our vision, as long as we understand that it – like us – will need continuous refinements.

And then, it means saturating our thinking by focusing time and time again on the beliefs, thoughts and feelings associated with that vision.

"Our manifestation, however, will only be sustainable if we have resolved our past, meaning that we have changed the limiting beliefs we held about ourselves. What this requires, as we have discussed at length, is to reach exclusivity in our thinking. Along the way, we must become intellectually and experientially aware of the treacherousness of any remaining subconscious beliefs of *not being good enough* and variations thereof, such as to consistently interrupt our conditioned patterns by observing ourselves and recognizing when they creep in. Otherwise, as long as these beliefs persist, they will continue to be creative, ultimately sabotaging the vision that we spent so much time and effort on.

"Come, I will show you."

He led me into the circle of stones at the top of the flattened hill. It was the first time we entered the archaic circle. He invited me to climb onto one of the large boulders in the east, and make myself comfortable, the rising sun wonderfully warming my back.

He walked towards the opposite side of the circle, cleared his voice, and announced, "Beloved Maya, spectator of the universal soul, let me present this morning's performance. It is a tragic tale, recounting the travails of the one who sought to build a clear fountain, without undertaking the archeological excavations into the depths of her mind that were needed to uncover the poison seeping into the soil. I call upon you to unfold the wings of your imagination in the all-seeing rays of the morning light and enjoy the spectacle."

He clapped three times, bowed and mischievously walked off the makeshift stage, to come and sit down by my side. I focused on the empty space that he left behind, intrigued, waiting to be surprised. By now, I was ready for anything.

Sure enough, as if answering the Sage's call, three crows came flying over and landed in the grass right where he had stood. They started pecking the ground and cawing loudly. As I stared at them, opening all my senses, at first I only saw three birds, walking around each other, flying off, coming back, and chattering. But suddenly, in their long shadows extending away from us onto the vertical slabs of stone forming a semi-circle at the back of the stage, the outline of human forms became apparent. And in their caws echoed the melody of human speech.

I marveled at the realization that the human forms dancing on the rocks were staging a play. A play of shadows. The tale of a woman and her dreams.

The first shadow, cast by the most imposing crow, took on the form of the narrator, and introduced Act I.

Once upon a time, there was a woman who was afraid to die in poverty. She lived in a small wooden shack, full of all the things she had collected throughout her life and was unwilling to let go, for fear that she might need them some day. Her main room was piled from floor to ceiling with all manner of scraps and pieces of cardboard, wooden debris and fragments of tile, countless chipped glass containers and the odd piece of string and cloth. Living amidst all these things would have been a challenge for anybody but the mistress of the house, who never tired of admiring her broken treasures and adding some more whenever she could lay her hands on an interesting object that someone else had discarded.

She would take it home and find the perfect place for it, in the eclectic amalgam that made up her crammed interior. "Oh this is just fine," she would say. "This is so fine." But no sooner had she set it down than she reverted to her initial fears, wondering how she could acquire just one more belonging, find one more thing to add. "You never know," she would mutter repeatedly, shaking her head from side to side.

And thus her life went on, until one day, a cousin came to visit. She wrinkled her nose and raised her eyebrows as she walked into what seemed like a graveyard of redundant objects. She turned to her cousin and said, "There is a wizard who lives in the forest on the other side of the hill. Why don't you go see him? Don't you want to live in a real house, a proper home? Look at this. You live in a wasteland. Maybe he can show you how to use his magic to attract a house into your life."

The very next morning, the woman set off, her little satchel on her back, and on the way, couldn't help collecting all the things she found, which might one day, you never know, be of use. The path was steep and the road was long, and her bag was getting heavier and heavier with every step. And she thought to herself: perhaps I can leave it here on the side of the hill, and take it home on my way back. Pleased with her smart idea, she set her bag onto a rock and lightly continued her journey to see the wizard.

As she walked, she started thinking about what she would ask him. If he knew magic, then he would certainly know how one could materialize a house. The house she had always dreamed of, vast and spacious, equipped with all the things she might need one day. The more she thought about it, the more she forgot to look for the little things she might be able to pick up on the way. And without even noticing it, she walked straight through the forest, covering the remaining distance in the blink of an eye, finding herself at the base of the steps leading up to the wizard's den.

An old man with a long white beard and a pointy hat was leaning on his stick, looking at her. "So," he said, before she had time to open her mouth, "You want a house, do you?" Her jaw dropped and she froze in fear. But the wizard smiled, and said, "I can show you how to use magic to manifest your wishes, if that is your desire?"

"Yes, yes!" she replied, "Please show me!"

The wizard sat her down under his magic tree and explained to her the laws of manifestation. He showed her how to create the house in her mind, by visualizing all its details and feeling into the sensations that she would experience by walking through the garden, up the stairs and through its many many rooms. He showed her how to take her mind from her clutter-filled shack into the splendor of that which she wanted to create.

She was very pleased and got ready to go, thanking the wizard with all the words she knew. "Not so fast," he said, "we are only half way there. You now must learn to tame your fears." But at the sound of that word, she shrieked and ran off as fast as she could, never turning back. She ran through the forest, and up the hill, grabbing her bag on the way down, you never know when you might need it, and all the way back into her shack. She locked the door behind her and finally stopped to catch her breath.

She was reassured. Now she knew how to use magic to attract a house into her life. What use was it to face her fears? Wouldn't they naturally be appeased by the sight of the mansion she was drawing up in her mind? She spent the following days and nights, for weeks and weeks, dreaming and visualizing the house. She saw every little detail, the gravel path, the embroidery on the chairs around the open fireplace, the chiseled stone steps leading up to her bedroom, the silks and the carpets, the wood and marble. She created it all piece by piece in her intensely focused mind. For the first time in her life, she forgot to amass small things, as she was building bigger ones with her imagination.

A month passed and one day, a man rang her doorbell. She peeked through a crack in the door and saw his fine clothing and princely air. Puzzled and slightly afraid, she opened the door.

"Lady," he said, "I have some grave news for you. Your great-great-aunt on your father's side has passed away."

She stared at him blankly, not knowing why he would come all this way to announce the death of an old lady she had never known.

"And," he continued, "all her heirs having died, she bequeaths her remaining possessions to you, namely a grand mansion set in a sumptuous park, on the shore of a lake, in the Northern Valley."

He showed her a long scroll that she couldn't read, handed her the keys, mounted his horse and galloped away.

Her jaw dropped as she looked at the keys in her hands, from which a small map was dangling with instructions on how to get there. For several days she sat motionless, unable to believe that she now really owned a house. She decided not to tell anyone, fearing that they might become jealous, and try to take it away from her. Perhaps she had better continue living in her shack, for who knows what could happen if anyone saw her in the big house.

But after a week, she couldn't hold her curiosity any longer. She took her satchel, the keys with the map, and off she went to the Northern Valley. On the way, she no longer collected the items she saw, waiting to see whether the house would provide for the things she might need. She followed the path around the last bend, and arrived at the lake. And there, on the other side, she saw the most wonderful mansion, the house of her dreams. She ran to the door, and as she walked in, saw that it was all there, exactly as she had created it in her mind: the gravel path, the embroidery on the chairs around the open fireplace, the chiseled stone steps leading up to her bedroom, the silks and the carpets, the wood and marble.

She laughed in joy and rolled on the floor and jumped to the skies, thanking the wizard in her heart for his wonderful magic. And as she did, she heard his booming voice, "Not so fast lady, you are only half-way there. You must still learn to tame your fears."

"Nonsense," she replied, "I have my house. What else could I want?"

She moved in and started exploring the many rooms and closets, the garden and the lake. There was so much space and so many things. Wonderful things, everywhere. And they were all hers.

As time passed and she had become acquainted with her new possessions, she slowly started wondering again: what if there was something missing, what if there was just that one additional object that she might need one day? What if it wasn't there? Slowly, her obsession started creeping back in, and she again took to collecting little bits here and there, adding them to her luxurious belongings. As time went by, little piles of scraps started emerging, scattered in the spacious corners of every room.

And thus her life went on, until one day, the man in fine clothing and a princely air appeared at the door of the mansion.

"Lady," he said, "I have some grave news for you."

She stared at him blankly, not knowing why he would come again, now that all matters had been settled.

"The land your house is on has been under dispute for quite some time. It has come to our unequivocal knowledge that it was never owned by your great-great-aunt. The rightful owner has gone to the king and been granted the right to recover his belongings. I request that you hand over the keys to me at once."

She took her satchel, swallowing her disbelief, handed him the keys, and walked back the long road to her little shack full of useless scraps. All the while, she shook her head, mumbling, "I knew it, I knew it, I am going to die in poverty." But before dying she wanted to see the wizard one more time, to angrily explain to him that his magic was no good, and that he was a fraud.

So off she went, up the hill and through the forest. The wizard with his long white beard and pointy hat was leaning on his stick, waiting for her. He raised his brows and pre-empted her fury, by saying, "Ah, so you think I'm a fraud, do you?"

He laughed and laughed, a roaring laugh that resonated in the far-off hills and sent a chill down her spine.

"Using the magic of the mind to manifest our dreams is easy. The hard part is to recognize them when they come, and then to hold on to them. And to do so, we must tame our fears, which means resolving our past. For as long as you keep thinking what you've been thinking, you'll keep getting what you've been getting, no matter how many detours you make along the way.

"You've been thinking that you are lacking something in your life, and that you will die in poverty. These thoughts have a magic power of their own, especially when you give them strength by carrying them around everywhere you go. You have been breathing them in and breathing them out at all times. And so, while the outer contours of the home you created with the power of your mind were magnificent, these thoughts did not disappear. They moved in with you and filled your new house with the energy of lack. By not tending to your fears, this energy continued to be creative in your life and worked its own magic... the manifestation of lack, which sent you right back home to your little shack."

The End.

The three crows lined up in front of us and bowed. I stood up on my boulder, clapping wildly, amused and impressed by their performance. They flew up, circled three times above our heads and disappeared.

I watched them go, and sat down again, enjoying the gentle warmth of the sun. I stared at the now empty stage in the middle of the stone circle, silently absorbing the teachings. The grass swayed in the breeze, and I could almost hear it whispering, as if the final words of the crow-wizard were still lingering in the air, a clue pointing to the next step in my journey: "… tame your fears… resolve your past… your own manifestation of lack…"

XIII

Rewriting the Script

Maya

I stood on the hillside looking at the ruins before me. The Sage had sent me off on my own, pointing towards the North, where after a short walk downhill, he explained that I would reach a plateau on which lay the remains of an ancient temple. He had instructed me to pay close attention to what I felt as I wandered into the site.

There was not much left of what he had called the temple. Many large rocks were loosely scattered around, and in one spot, I could still distinguish what might have been the base of a wall. It looked like the building had been round. As I approached, I was astounded to find a perfectly circular rock placed in the very center of the former structure. It was an enormous dark stone, slightly hollowed out, holding a pool of translucent rainwater. I felt irresistibly drawn to the stone's smooth shiny surface, and as I dipped my hands into the fresh sparkling water, my whole body started shaking.

It was like getting back in touch with the archaic elemental forces of nature, the primordial rock that preceded the waters of creation. As I ran my hands along its outer shell, I knew that I was touching a mystery, linked to an energetic source that our ancestors had known how to harness and honor, beyond what my mind could grasp. The longer I remained in that spot, connected with the world beyond the visible, the more my body felt revived, becoming lighter and stronger, all remnants of tiredness miraculously lifting away. It was as if I had just found an ancient mechanism designed to renew and restore depleted selves.

With a newly gained clarity, I sat down in the grass, intensely aware of my surroundings, noticing the particular shape of every rock, every blade of grass swaying in the wind, the buzz of insects, the smell of the warm earth. And suddenly, the veil parted. I was fully awake, fully lucid, and as had happened in my childhood, I experienced everything around me as myself. It was so beautiful and so strange at once. My mind was struggling to catch up with this experience of reality, which didn't fit into anything it knew, transcending its entire constructs based on viewing the self as a separate individual entity.

It only lasted a few minutes, and as it faded, I saw the Sage walking down towards me. Our eyes met; he understood. We both started laughing. "Why didn't anyone tell me about this?" I asked.

He laughed even more and said, "Even if we had, what would have been the point? Things become real only when they are experienced. All else is only an abstract idea, an out of reach concept laden with doubt and disbelief. But this is not about belief or disbelief, it simply is. Or it isn't."

"So," he continued, smiling, "now that you have regained your capacity to see, if I asked you to write the script of the next years of your life, what would you write?"

It was a huge question. I had come to the island searching for healing, wanting to recover my health so that I could continue living the life I had known. But now, everything looked very different. There was so much to process, so many pieces we had examined and turned upside down. How was I going to reassemble this baffling puzzle called my life? Especially now that reality had shown me an expanded version of myself.

"I don't know," I answered.

"Why don't you give it a try?" he encouragingly suggested. "You could start by thinking about what you imagine for yourself a year from now? How will you feel? What will you be doing? What will you be thinking? Who will you be with? Where will you be? The specifics of your work or the actual place where you might live are not important at this stage. What matters is the energetic and emotional tone that you want to create. This feeling tone will attract into your life circumstances that are resonant with it." He handed me a pen and a notebook and strolled off joyfully through the grassy field.

I smiled as I watched him go. How wonderful, I thought, that we have found each other on this little piece of land close to the skies. I breathed in, happy to be alive. And alive I was, with a blank piece of paper before me, ready to create the future I wanted, free from the limitations imposed by my own mind. And yet, that simple exercise soon proved much more difficult than I initially thought. If everything around me was really part of me, what did it mean to envision 'my' future? And if I took the more familiar view from within the confines of my physical body, which seemed to have an individual life of its own, what did that little 'I' want?

As I reflected on this question, I realized that just like the little girl who had stood before the Genie in the Sage's story, I had not been accustomed to acknowledging and tending to my own needs, particularly when simultaneously silencing all the voices that kept repeating: *No, that's not possible, you can't think that. No you can't possibly want that, and even if you did, you couldn't have it.*

I was stuck. I had thrown all the pieces of my life into the air, and was waiting for them to tumble back down so that I could pick them up and reassemble them in a brand new way. After a while, as I sat in the grass by the ruins, I saw the pieces slowly falling into my hands, and I witnessed myself sanding down the toxic layers of conditioning that I had taken on from the world around me, diligently scraping away all the false beliefs and interpretations born of fear and a lack of self-love. I understood that the new me would need no varnish, it would be raw and proud, its smooth wooden surface showing the veins of the Earth crisscrossing my being.

And suddenly it all became clear: my life could only be devoted fully and unconditionally to Her, the source of all wisdom, the very life flowing in my veins. After all, that's who I was. Times were different now, but I was still the Priestess of Gaia. I was her Oracle, embodying and serving the divine feminine. She was my body and I was hers, and that's how the little I connected to the expanded version of who I was: the Earth and all of creation.

Yes, a year from now I would be dancing barefoot in the grass, in honor of life. I would rejoice at the delicate spring blossoms as they offered their beauty to the rain and the sun, lovingly surrendering to the breath of impermanence. I would laugh and play. I would be wild and strong, gentle and soft. My body would be healed, full of energy, flowing harmoniously through the seasons, following the rhythm of the moon. I would honor myself, and I would honor Her, in every breath, every thought, every deed.

It felt wonderful, but there was a problem. A piece was missing. My vision was completely detached from my old reality. Here I was, sitting on an island in the middle of nowhere, and I had just created another one in my mind; the difficulty being that I saw no bridges granting me access to the life I had just envisioned. I thought about the crows' play of shadows, and how manifesting the future goes hand in hand with resolving one's past.

So what about my past? I felt like we had barely touched upon it with the Sage. He had shared many stories and I had gone into a deep exploration of my essence, seeking to understand who I am. But how could I relate all of this to the more down-to-earth material plane of existence? To the life I had led, and the life I was going to lead? Granted, I had seen how my confusion about the true nature of my being had made me look for love outside of myself, behaving in such a way as to gain the approval and affection of my adoptive parents; how walking down that path had ultimately led me to suppress my intuition in favor of a rational anaesthetized existence. I also understood that my body had sounded the alarm, refusing to continue living in the shadows of a severed mind.

I even saw how this pattern of suppressing the feminine had played out before, in a different scenario. Then, I had been afraid of being a woman, afraid of my power as a woman communing with the wisdom of the Earth. In this life, I had been afraid of giving a voice to the feminine, intuitive, feeling side of me. The stories were different, but the underlying pattern was exactly the same.

But what about the rest? What about my career choices? My work? My practically nonexistent relationships? How did it all come together, and how exactly was I going to reach what the Sage had called exclusivity of thinking? How exactly was I supposed to resolve my past and walk back into my life, consciously creating a new future?

The mere thought that I would have to leave this land, that I would need to go back to the place that had been my home frightened me, dampening the elated state I had enjoyed all morning. It was inconceivable. Yet I couldn't stay on this island forever, could I? I sighed deeply, noticing how easily my mind had created fear and pulled me out of joy and wellbeing. I reassured myself with the thought that there was more to learn, more to experience and more to understand. I vowed that I would stay until I was ready, until the path became clear. With that thought, I got up and wandered back to the fire pit, hungry for food, and hungry for more.

I shared a simple meal of fresh greens with the Sage. Magdalena was not with us. She had gone to the southern tip of the island. I was surprised to learn that there was a little village there with a weekly market. It appeared that the island was much larger than I had initially thought, and there were other people living on it. Furthermore, boats regularly made the journey connecting us back to the mainland. Perhaps we were not that isolated after all. Perhaps there was a way to build a bridge between my magic cave in the land of the mind and what appeared as the mundane banality of the world I had left behind.

The Sage looked at me. "So, you want to understand the missing pieces?" he asked, almost teasingly. I couldn't get used to the fact that he always seemed to know exactly what was on my mind. It was disconcerting, almost frightening. But he seemed to find my startled reaction highly amusing. "There is no mystery in what some might call the art of telepathy," he explained, "you already know that we are all connected. And it becomes even more intense when we are focusing together on the process of looking into the mind."

"Why don't we start with the missing piece in your story?" he continued. "Relationships. When you first arrived and I asked you to tell me your story, you spoke a long time, and you spoke about many things, but not once did you mention relationships, not once did you mention the existence or absence of a partner in your life, or your desire to build a family and have children, or not to have any children. This whole topic was conspicuously absent. Don't you find that interesting? Why don't you tell me more?"

I was taken aback. He was right. I had completely omitted the topic. Not intentionally of course. It simply hadn't seemed relevant. Before getting ill, I had a boyfriend. He lived on the other side of the country, and we had been seeing each other regularly for the past three years. I had met him on one of my business trips, through a colleague who came from the same city as him. He was attractive and fun and we had instantly enjoyed each other's company. Over time it seemed like there was potential for more. But the logistics of it proved difficult. It was not possible for me to be transferred to his city, and after all the time and effort it had taken me to reach my position, leaving my job was out of the question. On one of our holidays, as we dreamed about spending more time together, he had mentioned that he would be open to moving, that he could start searching for a job in my city. I don't know why, but I hadn't said anything, and we never spoke about it again.

Circumstances determined that we didn't see each other much after that. The last time I had flown out to see him, he had reproached me that I worked too much and that I wasn't even using up my holidays. He was right, and I sincerely wanted to spend more time with him. But I was busy; I was needed at work. I didn't know how it could be any different. I had concluded that my work was my life, and that if he wanted to be with me, he would have to accept that. Yet, after that last trip, we had stopped calling each other every day; the silences had gradually become longer, slowly pulling us apart.

In the early weeks of my illness I reached out to him again, desperately hoping that he would suddenly show up to take care of me, secretly wanting him to act as a fairytale prince who rescues the damsel in distress from the menace of imminent death. Of course, no such thing happened. Not only did he not come, but every time I called I got his answering machine. He never returned my calls. I was deeply hurt. I couldn't understand it. Even my friends showed more care than the man with whom I had envisioned sharing my life. The moment I needed him, he had vanished. Could it be that I had failed to see him for who he truly was? I ended up dismissing him from my mind, focusing on the challenging feat of simply surviving each new day.

The Sage nodded, pensively. "And before that?" he asked.

Well, there was not much before that, in any case no serious long-term relationship to speak of. The first man I fell in love with was married. He had been my teacher at university. For a year, I had sat there each week mesmerized by his every word, his presence, the tone of his voice. I had done everything I could for him to notice me, and he certainly had. It seemed that he was always intensely looking at me. Sometimes I even felt embarrassed, wondering if anyone else had noticed the longing in our interlocked gazes.

One evening, after class, gathering my courage, I had gone to his office at the time when he opened his doors to answer his students' questions. He had closed the door and stood before me, looking deeply into my eyes. He was so close that I could feel his breath on my cheeks. My whole body quivered. "Maya," he had said, "what do you want from me?" I noticed the slight tremor in his voice. "I don't know," I had answered. I didn't know what to say. I had been avidly seeking his presence, but had never indulged any thoughts beyond that simple yearning.

He had taken my hands in his and very gently, lovingly, his lips almost touching my skin, he had whispered, "If we had met at another time, if the circumstances had been different, perhaps we would have built our life together. And it would have been wonderful. But I have walked down the path of my life, I have made choices, and as it is now, it is simply not possible. Please understand." And with lowered eyes and hunched shoulders, he had grabbed his coat and bag, and practically run out the door without looking back, leaving me stranded, wanting more.

I looked at the Sage, saddened by my memories. It was clear to me that I wanted more in my relationships. But the more had never manifested. Time after time, I had felt abandoned. The funny thing was, it always seemed to happen before I even had a chance to engage in a serious long-term relationship with the man I was attracted to. As if the men I was interested in, were never quite available. As if I intentionally chose men who would desert me after a while, either because of the prevailing circumstances, or because I drove them away, by failing to fully invite them into my life.

"Yes," the Sage said, "you are starting to see. Continue looking, the patterns are revealing themselves to you. Remember: the early impressions made upon your mind led you to conclude that if you loved someone, he or she would abandon you. This fear of abandonment became a powerful creative force in your life. You made sure that no one got too close, for if they had, you would have been forced to face the fear of losing what you loved. And who wants to face their fears?

"And so, it was easier to keep men at arms' length, close enough to honor your desire for relationship, far enough to make sure you couldn't love them too much. In every case, the setup ensured that they would end up fulfilling your expectation of being abandoned. As is the case for all of us, you attracted the lovers who corresponded to your subconscious programming. And your programming said: *If I love someone, they will abandon me*, the ego emphatically adding: *as they have done before*. Thus, you chose to love men who were not available, and if they were, you made sure to push them away, squeezing the relationship until it eventually died. In your last relationship, as you became ill, you were more vulnerable, and perhaps ready to open up, but by then, it was too late. You had already driven your boyfriend away.

"And that brings us to another important piece of the puzzle, tightly linked to this one, namely your work. Tell me, why did you work so much? Why did you think that you were indispensable to your company? And why did it become the number one priority in your life? Beyond love, beyond relationships, beyond health and wellbeing, superseding all, destroying all in its conquering wake. It is important for you to understand this, as this very pattern is spreading like a disease across the lives of the men and women of your generation, curling itself around their throats, and choking our planet in the process."

The Sage was putting me on the spot. I was already upset with myself for having been so inept with my relationships. And now I felt judged, I was embarrassed and angry. I struggled to hold back my tears.

"This is not about you, Maya. I want you to learn to see things as they really are, without taking anything personally. It is essential for all of us to become compassionate observers of our minds, and have the capacity to laugh at ourselves, knowing that there are no mistakes. We are here to learn, and we are so much more than the little dramas we play; they are just a tool for us to grasp the magnificence of the human condition, and the incredible power of our minds."

I was deeply upset, avoiding the Sage's eyes, staring blankly at the horizon.

He looked at me and sighed, "We are all works in progress. I am exactly on the same path as you. It is no different. You are upset because you believe I am criticizing you. In my simple questions, you heard that I was challenging your choices and accusing you of that which you fear: of not being good enough. Please see that your emotional response is entirely dependent on your interpretation. If you had interpreted my words differently, you might be laughing now. But it is good that it is so, for whatever comes up is an opportunity for you to see your mind: it is an opportunity for healing."

The Sage sat down next to me and took me in his arms. Throughout my life, I had been uncomfortable with any form of physical contact, but in this instance, it was more than I could have asked for. I wrapped my arms around this peculiar man and cried all the tears I had never shed for those I had loved and lost. For what seemed the first time in my life, I allowed myself to be held, to be deeply unconditionally loved. I don't know if I fell asleep, or simply drifted into another dimension of soft eternity. I heard a song in the language of my ancestors. I couldn't understand the words, but somehow I knew that it told the wailing tale of one who has lost her beloved and seeks him on the highest peaks and in the deepest valleys, yearning for that most exquisite quality of absolute love, without ever finding the sought after human who could open up the stairway to the skies. It was the melody of unfulfilled longing, the wailing pain of separation from the source.

I felt someone wrapping a blanket around me. I opened my eyes, and saw Magdalena through the dancing flames, singing softly as she added more wood to the nascent fire. Her voice had brought me to a place so deep, so ancient, where I saw that I was simply one among many, eternally searching, finding and losing, learning the wisdom of Love along the way. And as I closed my eyes again, I suddenly felt that the arms holding me were the arms of my higher self, bathing me in the soothing energy of source.

After a long pause, the Sage broke the silence, "Would you like to continue?" he asked, handing me a glass of water.

"Yes." All of it was at once painful and comforting, perplexing yet insightful. It was as if he had taken me on an accelerated version of the rollercoaster of life, except that in this instance I was in the chariot whirling around the bends, and at the same time the spectator watching the scene from the sideline.

"You have been much too demanding of yourself," he said, "as if you thought that you needed to be perfect, in every moment, in every thought, in every act. As if that perfection would shield you from any form of criticism, leaving no opening for anyone to disapprove of you. Perhaps it would not be far-fetched to seek the origins of this attitude in your austere religious education. You mentioned that your father strove to model his life after that of Jesus, and that he seemed to expect you to do the same. If we model our lives after the son of God, the one who by definition was perfect, what are the chances that we will be disappointed in ourselves, that we will fail the standard we have set?"

As he said these words, I started hearing my father's voice and was taken back to a Sunday morning in church. He was preaching about the subject of doubt, and I saw him up there, standing in the pulpit, his finger raised towards the heavens. "How many times?" he shouted, "how many times did Jesus doubt?" His tone had become so menacing that the assembly of the faithful shuddered beneath him. "Only once!" he exclaimed, bringing his fist down with a thump. "A single tremor of doubt at the hour of death. Just one hesitation, one gentle plea, in his entire existence..." We were all holding our breath, wondering what would come next. After a long, heavy pause, he solemnly ended his sermon with the words, "May we be unflinching in following His example. May we be fervent in our prayers for forgiveness when we fail."

The Sage nodded, as if he had been sitting on the wooden church benches with me, "How reasonable is it that we would be able to emulate such an idealized version of ourselves? It is very unlikely, isn't it? The consequences are severe: we end up walking around burdened by a mantle of guilt for not having met our expectations, ignoring the simple truth that we had placed them out of reach. We choose to bask in the certainty of our sin, the engrained belief that we are tainted from birth, that we are simply *not good enough*.

"And then what happens? As we ferociously cling to the belief of our mediocrity, we seek that which takes us away from our pain. We dive into the vast amnesic fields of pleasure, where for one brief and glorious moment, we no longer feel the heavy rocks we tied to our ankles. Time after time, we come back to these fields, assiduously lapping up their golden promise, engaging in that which brings us pleasure like an addict following her urge for another line of coke.

"What brings us pleasure? At a most basic level, love brings us pleasure. It temporarily silences the inner voice whispering that we are not good enough. And when we are confused about our true nature, when we have smothered the self-love burning in our soul under layers of fear, guilt and shame, we seek that love in our external environment. And there, we often come to believe that approval is an expression of love. Thus, as we wander through the wastelands of our pain, we attempt to manipulate our external environment in such a way as to gain as much approval as possible.

"That is why so many people work day and night. I am not talking here about the men and women who need to struggle every day for their basic survival – that is another type of manifestation, which we will not delve into just now. What I am talking about are the people like you and so many others, who have found in their work a source of approval. Their professional endeavors bring them accolades from their colleagues and superiors, respect from their family and friends, rubbing a temporary balm onto their self-inflicted wound of unlovability.

"You, too, found that work was a mechanism through which you could get this love that you were yearning for. I would guess that as is often the case, it may even have started earlier, in school and later in the higher institutions of the intellect, where good grades represented a sign of achievement, the sign that you were a good girl who deserved to be loved. You studied hard and earned everyone's admiration, but already then, this mechanism was not sustainable. All the while, your inner voice kept saying: *you can do better.* And your teachers may have unknowingly exacerbated your entrenched urge for perfection, thinking they were doing you a favor by being overly demanding. In all likelihood, they were simply transferring onto you their own fear of not being good enough, by pushing you harder and harder, and making sure that whenever you achieved a set goal, the bar was immediately raised a little further.

"Whilst your inner voice quietly pulled you down, you thought you could outrun it by plunging wholeheartedly into work and becoming what society refers to as a leader. People looked up to you as a role model of what has come to be known as 'success'; you received praise, men eyed you with lust and admiration. You had an ever increasing budget that you could spend, giving you power over money and over the people around you, bringing with it increasing levels of approval. All of it simply became a mechanism by which your ego sought to control your external environment in such a way as to lead you away from pain and into pleasure.

"Of course, it was futile, for as you now recognize, the real source of your pain lay elsewhere. You probably weren't even able to believe the compliments showered upon you, the applause when you spoke in public, the spark of respect in your board members' eyes after you had concluded another deal that earned the company millions. The bar remained forever out of reach, and whatever anyone else may have said or even genuinely believed about you, you couldn't hear it. You coldly dismissed their praise and concluded that you should do better.

"And then, the stakes were raised even higher as the shadow of a newly empowered force loomed on the horizon: the fear of failure. The more success you got, the more power, the more money, the more recognition, the greater your fear of losing control over your life, as this would have plummeted you right back into the obscure well of your feeling of being unlovable, the sinister realms of pain that you so adamantly strove to leave behind.

"There was no turning back. You had to continue moving forward in what became an endless race to keep the flow of approval coming towards you. Your ego obediently complied, doing what it does best: focusing all its efforts on controlling the world around you in such a way as to continue creating a scenario that would feed your need for love. And that meant: earning more money, gaining more power, thus ascertaining more control over that which brought you more money, more power, and ultimately, more approval. Surreptitiously, what started as a relatively innocent attempt to find love by being a good student and an impeccable employee slipped out of your hands and became an uncontrollable urge. And that, my dear Maya, is the definition of the word addiction.

"Addiction is not just about drugs or alcohol, even if these are the most commonly recognized and socially unacceptable forms of it. An addiction is any uncontrollable obsession to use the external environment to change the way we feel internally, so that we may feel better. It may take the form of imbibing specific substances, be they drugs, food, smoking, or medication. But we can also become addicted to situations that impact our internal chemistry in specific ways and trigger emotions that we associate with pleasure. Work is one such situation. It can become a compulsive drive, keeping us in a perpetual state of striving for something which, by its very nature, is only temporary, and thus unsustainable.

"As this scenario took hold of your life, there was suddenly no time left for anything else. You may have sincerely thought that you wanted intimacy, that you wanted meaning in your life; part of you may even have been shocked to find that you willingly engaged in ethically questionable deals, but the irony was: you couldn't control it anymore. You had become addicted to work, and anything that might have pulled you away from it became dangerous because it lead you into a territory that your ego could not control. Relationships are always a perfect setting for us to come face to face with that which we fear most, for the sake of healing. In your case: your fear of being abandoned. And thus, not having enough time was a perfect excuse. You moved away from intimacy. You moved away from feelings and emotions, from all that was unpredictable and seemingly irrational, thus risky. You see, this is where we come full circle: you got trapped into an addictive work cycle, which urged you even further into repressing the feminine force suffocating within you, as you steadily clung to your illusory structures of exalted rationality and control."

The Sage paused for a while and looked at me. Every single word he had spoken had hit home. I felt nauseous from the contemplation of the dire reality of my existence. And then, to make it even clearer, he added, "Tell me, Maya, what happened when you became sick? When it all started falling apart, and you realized that you would no longer be able to go to work? What was your reaction? What was the reaction of the people around you?"

I had difficulty responding. It was bad enough without having to revisit these unpleasant weeks, but I totally remembered, and I knew why he was asking.

I had panicked. At first, I denied what was going on. I pretended that everything would be back to normal within days. That's what I kept telling my assistant every time I called him. I felt guilty for all the work that wasn't being done, for letting everyone down, for not having been up to the task. I even tried to sit in front of my computer, but couldn't focus on the screen – it was all a blur and gave me incapacitating migraines. But I kept trying, despite the pain, unwilling to come to terms with the fact that I physically couldn't do it. And then, after a while, the amount of work left undone and the responsibilities I had not honored became so great that I couldn't face any of it anymore. I cowered and fled into the frail shelter of my disease.

As for the people around me, my mother pretended that I wasn't sick. She acted as if nothing had changed, calling me every day to ask if I was feeling better. It was as if I didn't have the right to be sick, as if I needed to continue working and being the successful woman that she wanted me to be, for my own sake. She even said something about me stopping this psychosomatic nonsense and getting out of bed. It infuriated me. I couldn't believe she really thought I was pretending. As if I could just switch myself back on after a momentary blackout.

At times, as I lay in my bed, I could hear my father, his finger raised towards heaven, admonishing me, "Jesus was never sick. Why are you sick? What happened to you? How dare you fail us?" I had failed. I had failed to comply with the perfect image of how I thought I needed to be in order to receive love. It was a scenario in which being sick was simply not allowed. The specter of my unlovable self paraded before me, holding hands with the elusive shadow of my shame.

"Yes," the Sage nodded, "isn't it fascinating how everyone around you was sending you back the exact reflection of your own beliefs about yourself? Do you see to what extremes your body had to take you to rip you away from your addiction? It had to practically take you to the verge of death for you to even start listening. Isn't it insane how far we need to go for the sake of coming to know ourselves? Do you understand now, how it all fits together?"

I saw it all. And there was nothing more I wanted to say. We sat in silence, watching the flames burning into the night. The crackling fire of purification, utterly painful, melting away all that was no longer needed, ablaze with the promise of what was yet to come.

XIV

Finding my Mother

Maya

I barely slept that night. I sat outside by the entrance to my cave, thinking through my entire life, my decisions, my actions, my relationships, my family, my work. I looked at it all again and again, with the fresh perspective and depth that I had gained from the day's conversations.

I had moments of utter fascination, feeling incredibly free, where I looked through all the layers that composed my self, my life, my choices, as if looking at another person, detached of any emotions, amused and deeply at peace. There were no mistakes. There was no death. There was no fear, no confusion. There were only beliefs, arising from our interpretation of the events in our lives, and these beliefs created our reality. I looked at my mind and saw a highly networked three-dimensional constellation of thousands of beliefs, linked to each other. A living mind in constant change, abandoning obsolete pathways in the blink of an eye and creating new ones, reinforcing or weakening the core central nodes in the process. I was in awe as I looked at my mind playing the game of being human, and I celebrated the perfect beauty of my imperfection.

At the same time, however, I periodically slipped from these states of amused bliss into a chaotic cauldron of emotions, stirred up by having looked at all the aspects I least liked about myself, all the things that hurt most, precisely because they were a testimony to the reality of my imperfection. And that word was still a painful thorn in my side. My deeply held belief that being imperfect meant *being unlovable* was still coming up for air, resisting the irrevocable death sentence pronounced by my newly seeing eyes. Indeed, as the Sage had cautioned, the new bud of absolute self-love needed to be tenderly nurtured. It needed time to blossom.

And in the meantime, I was angry. Angry at my foolishness and my addiction to work, my tenacious fear of being abandoned and the consequences of this. Angry at my birth mother for having abandoned me in the first place. Angry at my adoptive parents for having withheld the truth for so long. Angry at all those who had been around me all these years for their ignorance, for having kept me in the dark about the nature of the mind, and for their ridiculous, destructive, self-serving tendencies. I was even angry at the Sage for having torn my ego to pieces. Ironically, I wanted to blow things up.

I went to bed late, furiously turning from side to side, wavering between a fuming urge for destruction and a state of compassionate amusement. Shortly before dawn, I eventually fell asleep, exhausted. I had many dreams, their fragments tumbling into each other upon awakening. I remembered several undecipherable pieces: running through the snow, trying to escape from a man who threatened to kill me. Hurrying to complete a huge mosaic of tiny black and gold square stones, on the floor of my office, in the shadow of my boss arrogantly reclining in my chair. Throwing the pieces into the air and running out screaming, "No!" Standing on a cliff by the sea, suddenly becoming lucid in my dream. Deciding to jump in to see whether I could breathe under water. Sitting on the sea floor, astonished to be breathing amidst the seaweed, and suddenly hearing the Sage's voice, "There is more. There is always more!"

I blinked trying to make sense of the fragments, repeating these words in my mind. It felt as though I had gone through a complete dismembering, blowing to pieces everything I thought was me and my life, coupled with a deep remembering and reconstruction, the shape of which I was only starting to fully taste and embody. Could there really be 'more'? More to understand, more to analyze, more to dissect about myself? Just the thought of it exhausted me. I didn't want to see the Sage. I didn't want any more information. I just wanted to be left alone. I crawled out of the cave. It was late. And there, on the platform, lay a beautiful plate of food, as if the Sage had left me a note inviting me to spend some time on my own. It infuriated me. Why did he always have to know everything? The turmoil from the previous night was still bubbling inside me, and I sat down, staring at the horizon, wondering what would happen next, almost challenging life by refusing to believe that there could possibly be more.

After eating, I went for a walk in the hills. I felt hazy from the lack of sleep and it was good to move my limbs, become aware of my breath and feel my heart beat. I arrived at a grove of trees close to the water. I hadn't noticed it before. It felt very peaceful. I lay down under the trees in the long golden grass, and as I looked up at the sky through the swaying leaves, I felt nostalgic for my birth mother. I missed her. Perhaps there was more after all. Yes, I had one more question: What had happened? Why had she forsaken me?

The sky became blurry as the tears formed in my eyes. The pain was still there. The pain of human separation. The pain of not understanding how she could have been so cruel. I closed my eyes, diving into the deep sadness, wondering whether – as in my dream – I would be able to breathe under the vast ocean of my tears. And suddenly, before I could attempt to draw the first breath, there she was.

She was a young woman, with golden skin and long black hair, just like mine, shining in the light of my vision. Her presence sparkled with life, and yet seemed shrouded in a veil of grief. She stretched her arms towards me and spoke.

Maya. My dear child. How I understand your anger and your sorrow. How I wish things had been different. How I wish I could have kept you, and seen you grow up to become the beautiful woman that you are. Sadly, by the time you were born, I believed that giving you away was the only thing I could do to save you. It was the hardest thing I ever did. And one of the last. It broke my heart. You asked to know, and I have come to tell you the story of our people, the story of the land of your ancestors, so that you may understand, and hopefully forgive us. Hopefully forgive me.

It all started shortly after I was born. I, like you, first opened my eyes in the forest, onto the lush greens that were our home, close to the big river, beneath the clouds. From the beginning, I was taught the ways of the forest. I was taught how to protect myself from harm, how to gather and prepare our food, and how to tend to the plants and the animals. I spent my early years living a simple life in harmony with the rains and the sun, learning from the elders of our community how to become a guardian of the Earth's generosity.

What I loved most was to play in the tumbling streams that wound their way down to the big river. With my older brothers, we would jump into the clear pools and lie down on the warm rocks watching the waters whirl past. I would see all kinds of creatures as I lay there, sometimes waiting motionless for hours until I spotted a snake gracefully sliding through the branches. I was never afraid, feeling deeply connected to everything around me. When the rains came, the streams turned into roaring rivers tearing apart anything they encountered along their path. The noise was breathtaking. It was too dangerous to go in, but I would stand on the banks and watch, feeling through all my senses, letting the awesome power of the water flood my being.

One morning, as I walked back to our home to help with the cooking, I saw my father – your grandfather – standing by the front door of our small wooden shelter with a group of men from our community. They were talking loudly and seemed agitated. My mother was inside, going about her chores, listening attentively. A few days later, she announced to us children that our father would be working for a company that was settling in our area. I didn't really understand what it meant. On my walks through the forest, I hadn't seen anything different. Our mother explained that this would bring many good changes to our lives. She said she would be able to send us to school and buy us some shoes. My older brothers were elated, not so much about the school, but about the shoes. It was all very confusing to me. Everyone looked happy, but for some reason, I was absolutely terrified, as if I sensed deep inside that something had just been broken.

A few months later, I started going to school, quickly discovering what that was all about. It was puzzling, but I enjoyed learning to decipher the letters of the alphabet and running home to read proudly to my mother anything I could get my hands on, from old newspapers to the labels on some of the products brought in from the city. She always laughed and praised me. As she had promised, I also got my shoes. They felt tight and suffocating to my little feet, and I much preferred to feel the warmth of the earth as I walked. But I wore them to school because it was a sign that we were no longer what my teacher had called "poor".

Most of the men in the community had gone to work for the mysterious company. What had been a small settlement soon became a growing village with the arrival of many other families whose fathers were also employed there. It was exciting and I made new friends. We children went to school and the women tended to the households and the gardens. I was still allowed to play in the streams and run barefoot through the forest, looking for snakes. Our house got a new roof, which didn't leak during the heavy rains and we got electricity. The years passed and we were happy.

But slowly, strange things started happening. On my walks deep into the forest, I sometimes came upon large areas that had been cleared. It was horrible to see all these trees lying dead. I couldn't understand it. I would stand there, shaking and crying, witnessing what to me was nothing short of a massacre. I could feel their pain run through my body, sense the life vanishing from their mighty trunks, as they bled their last drops of sap into the red earth. At other times, on days that were otherwise clear and sunny, I would hear thunder in the distance and feel the earth shake under my feet. I begged my father to explain it to me, but he ignored my pleas. He would just stare at me with a distant look, which scared me even more. And so, I eventually stopped asking, no longer daring to venture too far from home.

One day, as I came to the big river, there was a pungent smell. I noticed a strange shimmer on the surface, as if someone had used a handful of oily colors to paint a top layer onto the water. It was dark and shiny. My whole body tightened, instinctively warning me to stay away. But I couldn't help dipping my hands in, intrigued by the thick slimy texture, soon noticing that it wouldn't come off. I tried to wipe my fingers in the grass, but to no avail. I started running along the banks with dripping fingers, anxiously trying to understand what it was, until I saw the silvery white bellies of countless fish floating dead on the surface. And there, right by my feet, a bird was stuck with spread wings in the dark sludge. I pulled it out, but it was too late. Its delicate body, coated in the sticky substance, lay stiff in my hands, two legs accusingly pointing towards the sky. I shuddered. It was a bad omen. I put it down onto the grass and ran up to my house as fast as I could to look for my mother.

By evening, the whole village was down by the river, including the men who had come back from work. It was complete chaos. Everyone seemed to be talking at once. But one thing became very clear. The shimmering layer and the dead fish and bird had to do with the new company, and they kept repeating the same word: oil. I was frightened, but my father said not to worry. He said that the rains would cleanse the river and that the fish would come back. He was right. Initially, they did.

We quickly forgot the incident and life seemingly returned to normal. I continued going to school, and soon became interested in boys, shifting my attention away from the forest and the streams, thinking less and less about the dead trees. A few years later, I married a young man from the village. He was older than me and had just started working for the company. I quickly became pregnant – I had just turned fifteen. For us in the village, this was nothing unusual. I had fully embraced my new life as wife and mother-to-be, and was excited about the prospect of having a baby.

But the baby never came. After a few months, I started bleeding. My husband went out in the night to find the village midwife. I was scared. I thought I was dying. The woman came and reassured me that I would live. But I had lost my child. It happened again and again. Three times. I lived through each ordeal with renewed hope, only to find my illusions crushed and my body exhausted. I didn't understand what was happening to me. Had I done something wrong? Had I disrupted the harmony of life to such an extent that I deserved to be punished? I started talking to others around me, asking for help. And suddenly, countless stories sprang forth from the bushes. It was as if everyone had kept quiet the terrible things happening to them, hoping they were isolated cases of no consequence. But as I voiced my concerns, they were echoed by others, relieved to finally have a chance to speak.

I learned that many recently married girls had also lost their babies. I learned that more and more villagers were suffering from strange rashes on their skin. Many complained of headaches and nausea, things that none of us had experienced before. Our domestic animals were behaving strangely and losing their young. There were more sightings of dead fish floating in the river. And many of the beautiful birds and wild creatures that had been our companions in the forest could no longer be spotted. People had explained it on the grounds that the village had grown, that we had scared them away, but that was clearly not the whole story.

There were rumors of all sorts, mostly stories of sorcery, allegedly accounting for the fact that our village had been cursed. Some people said that all could be resolved with the help of the powerful shamans who lived in the highlands. Others pretended that we just needed to wait and everything would soon come back to normal. My husband kept repeating that the company would "clean it up" and that there was nothing to worry about.

I didn't believe him and my instinct never lied. I remembered my hesitancy to embrace the good news when my father had announced he would work for the company many years earlier. It was becoming increasingly clear to me that not only were the trees being killed and the animals no longer reproducing, slowly but surely, we were all being poisoned. There was no doubt anymore. It was because of the oil. But why wasn't anyone doing anything about it?

I became afraid of eating the fish we caught, afraid of drinking the water. I no longer bathed in the streams. If the options shown to us by our brothers and sisters of the wild, creatures of the earth, water and sky, were to leave or to die, what was I to do? To whom could I turn? I felt helpless. The day I lost my third baby, my world collapsed. Life no longer made any sense. I just wanted to bleed to death and fall into eternal sleep. I begged the Pachamama to take me back to her. But she didn't. It wasn't my time yet.

To make matters worse, my husband was not receptive to my pleas. He was angered by what he said were hysterical accusations. He kept on saying that we ignorant women were good for nothing, that we always exaggerated everything. The people he worked with, they knew. They were scientists, educated people, he said. They had assured him that we had nothing to worry about. They had explained that our problems were not because of the oil, but because of our primitive lifestyle, because we lived on earthen floors and washed our clothes and ourselves in dirty water full of diseases. Besides, we owed them for all the good things that had come with the company: the roads, the electricity, the money. How could I dare complain? The more I suffered, the more aggressive he became.

Your father and I were so different. When we had met, he was still a boy, gentle and somewhat shy, curious about life, with a constant smile on his lips. I had been seduced by his smile, imagining it to be an open door onto a world of laughter and joy, the simple harmonious life I dreamed of. How quickly he had changed! He was very skilled in his work, smart and utterly dedicated. He soon gained the respect of his manager, along with more and more responsibility. Alas, with it, his insecurity turned into arrogance, as if he had raised himself to a superior class of people, giving him the right to denigrate the rest of us. He aspired to what he called a developed life, the life of the men and women he saw on our newly acquired television, the white people of the big cities. He didn't even want to speak our language anymore, expressing himself exclusively in the language of those who had come with the oil. In short, he looked at everything that belonged to our past, to the customs of our people, with utter contempt, seemingly forgetting the color of his skin and the blood that flowed in his veins.

I was deeply upset, yet did not dare challenge him. The rift between us widened every day. I silently blamed him for what was happening to us all. He had become an accomplice to those who had come to pillage our land. Every day, to my utter disgust, he found a reason to justify their actions. I too was no longer a child, but I still felt connected to my roots. I still wanted to speak the language of the forest. I still wanted to walk barefoot and listen to the music of the streams. I could not dismiss my heritage. I belonged to the forest. It was as simple as that. And in my anger and despair, I vowed that if she died, so would I.

I woke up one morning and I knew I was pregnant again. I was seized by a great panic. Despite my wish for eternal sleep, I wanted this child to live. If she had come to me, she deserved a better fate than that of her aborted brothers and sisters. I understood in that moment that I would never forgive myself for staying in my village, patiently waiting for death to take her. I had to leave. I had to find help. I stayed in bed for a long time, considering the options before me.

As I stepped out of the house, I saw the young man from the village who had recently lost his wife. She had suffered from a strange sickness for many months, and one night, she was taken away to a clinic several hours down the new road. She never came back. They said it was a curse. He was inconsolable. He had stopped working and roamed around day and night, uttering incoherent sentences, sleeping outside on the bare ground, living off the food people gave him. They said that he had lost his mind. I knew him well. We had often played together as children. His family had come from the village of the shamans, up in the highlands on the other side of the mountains, those mysterious snow-capped peaks that we could not see, but that were said to rise behind the hills on the flanks of our valley.

His presence in front of my home in that very instant drew my attention. A shiver ran through my body. Could it be a sign? I called him, inviting him to share my breakfast. It was risky. A machete was dangling from his belt and his behavior was unpredictable. I was alone, my husband already at work and most of the villagers out of sight, busy with their tasks. He looked at me hesitantly, as a wild animal sniffing me out, assessing the danger. We were so similar. It made me laugh. He heartily joined in, diffusing any tension, suggesting that he perhaps wasn't that crazy after all. He came into the courtyard and ate in silence next to me, his head balancing from side to side, occasionally emitting low grunts.

I stared at him sideways, intrigued, wondering whether I should ask. "The village of your ancestors," I said, "do you remember where it is?" He took one look at me. A long intense glance. A look that made my heart beat faster, without me knowing whether it was of fear or of joy. And he said, very distinctly, with a sudden determination, "I will take you there."

No sooner had we finished eating than he stared into the void, with a strange smile, and added, "We should leave now. Let's go!"

And we did! We marched out that very instant. I didn't even leave a note behind. I grabbed some food, and a shawl, closed the doors of the house, and set off behind a man who might as well have been leading me straight to hell. Somehow, it didn't matter. I had to leave. It was my only chance. We took a small familiar trail, winding its way upstream, through lush green vegetation in the direction of the mountains. After a few hours we left the stream and entered unchartered territory. I had never ventured beyond that point. The trail was getting steep, but my companion barely slowed down. Machete in hand, he relentlessly cut a passage through the thick underbrush, never looking back. I diligently followed.

After what seemed an eternity of slow progress, we emerged out of the brush onto a ridge with a plunging view over the whole valley. He pointed in the direction we came from and simply said, "Look!" I turned and gasped at the sight before me. I was exhausted from the effort, drenched in sweat and dust, my arms and legs scratched and red from the thorns and bugs. And what I saw in that instant almost finished me off. We had reached quite an elevation. To our right, the forested hills rolled off and away as far as the eye could see. But there, straight below us, the valley that had been my home now appeared as the last frontier of green on the edge of a series of open wounds, a succession of large stretches of land where the trees had been removed. I could just make out the infrastructure built on the extraction sites, dotted with dark pools seemingly cursing the skies. The lacerations of the road cut through these bare ashen patches, along with the pipelines, disappearing into the distance, towards the big city beyond the hills.

I sat down, unable to take in the devastation before me. Seen from above it was so much bigger, so much more dramatic than what I had expected. My companion was sitting next to me, his body rocking back and forth, moaning, as if in severe pain. I had picked some fruit along the way, on the familiar initial stretch, and offered him some. We ate quickly, mechanically, lost in thought. I didn't want to stay there any longer, nor did he. Without a word, we both turned our backs to the valley and set off again, haunted by the grim shadow of what we had just witnessed. Like the oil that had stuck to my skin when I dipped my fingers into our soiled river, I would never be able to rid myself of that image.

Night was falling. We both knew our ways in the forest, and quickly found a spot to set up our camp. We had been climbing for quite some time and were getting closer to the clouds. It was becoming increasingly humid. The forest was teeming with life, bursting with sounds and smells. I wasn't used to it anymore, but eventually managed to find sleep. I woke up in the middle of the night, and opened my eyes to find my guide leaning over me, staring at me. I screamed. He jumped, startled, and ran away. A little later, I saw him come back, and sit down further away, under a tree, rocking back and forth. He covered his face with his hands, repeating the same words, again and again, "She's dying, she's dying." Who did he mean? It scared me.

On the second day, we hit the fog. It was eerie and beautiful at once. We couldn't even see the tips of the trees, and water was dripping everywhere. The temperature dropped. It gradually became cooler but also easier to walk, the vegetation thinning out in places. Suddenly we arrived at what seemed a wide stone-paved trail. He pointed at it and simply said, "The Inca." I sighed with relief. There was no doubt anymore: he knew where he was taking me. We had arrived at the famous ancient trail that would lead us all the way to the pass in the snow and back down again to the plateau of the highlands.

We followed the trail of rock and grass, slowly leaving behind the thickness of the forest, to enter a more arid terrain of shrubs and bushes. The fog cleared as we climbed steadily higher and higher, until we completely pierced the clouds. Suddenly, the eternal snows unveiled themselves before us, their icy slopes shining in the sun, their ragged crests reaching into the blue skies. Beneath us lay a vast ocean of fog, hiding from view the numerous hills we had climbed and the memory of our valley and its open wounds bleeding in their folds. I was getting tired and we decided to stop again, enjoy the soothing rays of the evening sun and the magnificent sight of our ancestors of rock and ice. We would undertake the final ascent at dawn, and he assured me that we would reach his hometown by nightfall of the next day.

We set off before the sun had come out, in the light of a waning moon. The trail was wide and easy to follow, with the remnants of ancient steps built by the peoples who had conquered the highlands and sought to connect their empire across the mountains. It was very steep and I was losing my breath quickly, but the rare beauty of the scenery kept me going. After many hours of slow progress through increasingly bare rocky slopes, we reached the snow. I tasted the white crystals that had come from the heavens and cried tears of joy. I felt like I had entered a different world. A world of magic and mystery. A world where I could start dreaming again.

Finally, we reached the pass at the top of the world, between two imposing giants whispering of eternity. We peeked over onto the other side and saw a rugged landscape of browns and grays, descending abruptly onto the plateau of the highlands. Barely perceptible in the distance were the deep blue waters of the mystical lake. I had heard the tales of these lands, passed down to me by my grandparents. The tales of our ancestors who had sprung out of these waters at the origin of creation.

After the pass, my companion noticeably changed. He seemed to stand more erect, no longer mumbling to himself, nor swinging his limbs and hands in strange repetitive movements as he walked. He no longer avoided my gaze, looking straight at me when we stopped for a break. His eyes were unusually clear, almost transparent, cleansed of the dull glare that had masked his light for so long. There was a sense of relief, of harmony restored. Even his stride was different as he effortlessly floated down the mountain. I too, felt a sudden upsurge of energy, as if the snows had purified us, freeing us from the ghosts of the past.

By nightfall, as he had promised, we arrived at his village. Having left behind the arid slopes of rock and snow, we had entered a much more hospitable landscape of terraced fields and gentle trees. I was overjoyed to hear the familiar and merry sounds of life in a small village. A clear stream rustled by. Pigs and chickens roamed around, dogs barked and children chased each other, giggling. As we entered the village, we ran into his uncle, a cheerful man with a broad smile. After an initial moment of surprise and numerous questions about me, he warmly welcomed us, leading us to his house where his wife prepared some food and laid down straw mattresses for us to rest. Only then did I notice that my feet were hurting badly; I had pushed myself to the verge of exhaustion. But I was at peace, profoundly happy for the first time in years.

On the third day, having recovered from the journey, I went to see one of the shamans. He was sitting on a small wooden stool in his adobe house, in a room full of dried plants and offerings of all sorts. There were colorful woven cloths laid out on the floor for us to sit before him. He was an old man, with a bright light in his eyes, a toothless grin, and a noticeable bulge in one of his cheeks, where a ball of coca leaves was slowly being chewed. He started the invocations and proceeded to throw out the dried coca leaves on the cloth between us, to read my fate.

We did not speak the same language and my companion translated the words uttered by the shaman, punctuated by long pauses as he stared at the patterns created by the fallen leaves, "You are carrying a child," he said, "a very old soul." He suddenly became very excited, and added, "The bolt of lightning, the mark of the shamans… She is one of us… Maya. A bridge between worlds, between lands, between peoples."

"Will she survive?" I asked, trembling.

"It is not certain. The poison is flowing in your blood… If you go back to your home, you will both leave the world of the middle… I see another path for her, a path that will take her far away, and back one day… For you, it will be difficult. You cannot follow her. The Pachamama has heard your pleas. She is hurting. She is willing to take you back…"

I shuddered as I heard these last words. Upon arriving in the village I had caught myself dreaming that a simple peaceful life for me and my child might still possible. The shaman's reading had just shattered my hopes… but all had not been said yet.

He ended with another stream of invocations and handed me two large cardboard plates replete with the symbolic offerings I was to burn that same day. The central piece of each consisted of an aborted llama fetus, surrounded by bright pieces of wool and what seemed like colorful balls of sugar, along with an assortment of sacred herbs and dried flowers. The first was for me, and the second for my unborn child. The way they burned, he explained, would indicate whether my offerings were received, and reveal our respective fortunes in their ashes.

I decided to burn them at dusk, on my own, by the stream that came down next to the village. This is what I had come for, and now was the moment of truth. I set fire to both offerings simultaneously, side by side. I sat down on a large rock by the flowing water, and watched the strange fetuses melt in the flames. Yours, my dear Maya, burnt down completely, cleanly vanishing into silver ash. The offering had been accepted. The sacred llama had given its life for a new life to be born. You were to live! What a joy. Mine, however, did not burn. Somehow, the contorted fetal form remained intact amidst the flames and endured when all else had vanished and the embers died down. The message was clear. I would bring you to life, but I wouldn't be there to take care of you. I regretted my own words, my desperate plea, "If the forest dies, I want to die with her." But it was too late.

The ensuing months were unspeakably difficult. The more you grew in my womb, the more I loved you, the more I denied the reality of my fate. But with the pregnancy, I became increasingly ill. Life was draining out of me. I clung to it with all my might, determined to give you the last sparks of it. I so wished for you to experience the unspoiled beauty that I knew still existed in this world of ours. With every second, with every breath, I blessed you. I prayed for you to be loved and well taken care of after I was gone.

I was generously cared for by the family hosting us. But the night the shaman had spoken, my companion had come down to the river to witness the outcome of the offerings. He took one look and disappeared into the night. He was gone for several weeks, and after he came back, he avoided me as if I were the devil in person. In the silence of our journey through the mountains, we had bonded deeply, and I understood that he could not bear to see another woman he loved struggle to her death. He had come back to his village yearning for a new life, only to find that his shadow had followed: me, the specter of the past, a symbol of all those to be slain on the merciless altar of oil.

It was not my intention to inflict this pain upon him; he had been too kind to me. But I had nowhere else to go. So I waited for you to come. I sewed your name, the one given by the shaman, onto a beautiful blanket, along with my love and the memory of all I held dear. On the night of the Willakuti, I felt you coming. It was only befitting that you would have chosen to come on the night when the peoples of the highlands celebrated the return of the sun. I went out under the stars by the river, and gave birth beneath the trees. They weren't our lush trees pulsating with life, they were dry and resistant, but regardless, I wanted you to see their fine beauty when you first opened your eyes. I sang the whole time, instinctively knowing how to guide you into this world with my voice. It was the most beautiful moment of my life.

I wrapped you in the blanket and gathered the last of my strength. I knew I had little time left. I was too weak to walk, so I stole a donkey, asking for forgiveness, and set off in the direction of the big city of the fallen stars. I had heard of a place where you would be taken care of; where you would be given another life, far away from the toxic reality of your home.

She fell silent, her presence flickering in my mind. I was shaken with emotion.

"What happened to you afterwards?" I asked, trembling.

"I was heartbroken and in much physical pain. I dragged myself away, back out onto the land. I lay down and waited for the

Pachamama to take me." She smiled sadly, bringing a touch of light onto her tragic ending, as she whispered, "But you know, death is nothing but another door."

"And what about my father?" I added.

"I don't know, Maya. He never knew of your existence. But he would be proud of you. In a certain way, you fulfilled his dreams. And so am I, but for different reasons. No matter how difficult it was, I would do it all over again and even more to bring you to life. You truly are a beam of light."

XV

The Collective Field

Maya

I went to look for the Sage to tell him about my vision. He had been right. We form beliefs based on our interpretation of events. We make assumptions. And then we build our whole life on these assumptions, these interpretations and their corresponding beliefs. We create a whirlwind of emotions that go along with them and lose ourselves in the process, thinking we are the victims of our circumstances. And then, one day, the light goes on, as we discover that we were wrong, as we gain new information and see that the conclusions we drew were unfounded. My mother had never abandoned me. Physically she had left me, but bringing me to the city was her ultimate act of love. She had loved me deeply and unconditionally from the very beginning. She had loved me so much that she had been willing to leave her entire world behind and bravely walk into the unknown to bring me to life. In this human arena where I was playing, there had in fact been no grounds for me to believe that

I was unlovable, except in my mind.

But I was deeply disturbed by my mother's story. If we truly create our own reality, why did my mother have to suffer such an ordeal? She had been a kind and loving woman, deeply connected and devoted to the forest. How would the Sage's mind theories be able to explain her agony, justify the destruction and raping of her land, her slow poisoning and ultimate death? Surely, she wouldn't have written such a script for her life, even subconsciously. It simply didn't make sense. And this appeared to me as the most critical question. It threatened the consistency of all the teachings I had so willingly absorbed over the past few days on the island.

I started climbing to the top of the hill and saw them in the distance, wandering down towards the lake. The Sage turned and saw me waving at him. I caught up with them, out of breath, agitated by my thoughts. I shared my mother's story as we walked, along with my questions and doubts, blurting it all out in one unbroken stream of words. Even if the Sage already knew, as he always seemed to, I needed to speak it out, with all the anger and frustration it had stirred up in me. We arrived at a small rocky outcrop, on one of the lower hills, with a view of sunny fields rolling down to the water.

"This is very important," the Sage said, as he stopped and turned towards me. "Why did your mother have to suffer as she did? Why did her land, your land, have to be destroyed? If we truly are the creators of our own lives, was this a manifestation of her mind? And if not, are all my teachings mere puffs of smoke, evaporating at the slightest challenge? Let us look at it in detail, piece by piece.

"I would guess that your mother came into this life with her own lot of issues to work on in the process of her spiritual evolution. But even if she hadn't, even if we assumed that she came and grew up in a state of pure bliss and absolute self-love, feeling connected to everything around her, as she recounted to you, something changed dramatically the moment she lost her first child. She was in shock, terrified, believing she was bleeding to death; in this highly emotionalized state, her mind formed an association between childbirth and death – not only the death of her child, but also her potential death. Then it happened again, and again: pregnancy followed by death, strengthening this association to a near certainty, plummeting her into deep despair.

"As if that wasn't enough, during her third miscarriage, having lost any taste for life, she consciously formulated the wish to die and asked the Pachamama to take her. When it didn't happen, she intensified her plea. She saw the dead trees and the dead fish, she was aware that the wild animals were retreating deeper into the forest, she heard other people's stories of inexplicable suffering. She concluded that the shadow of death was real, that it was imminent and that there was nothing she could do about it. To leave or to die; those were the options. Initially, she didn't think she was sick. Yet, devastated by the reality unfolding around her and her incapacity to bear a child, in defiance of life, she vowed to die with the forest, to fall with the last trees. This was her wish, her intention, a powerfully creative thought. And wherever we focus our attention tends to expand in our life.

"But, you might say, that's beside the point. What difference does it make to want to die or want to live when there is clear evidence that the water you drink and the food you eat is slowly poisoning your system, interfering with the correct functioning of your organs? What I would answer is that no matter the external circumstances, and perhaps especially when these are dire, the thoughts we hold make a fundamental difference. Energy comes before matter. Our mind shapes our body. When we are anchored in thoughts of harmony and health, wellbeing and bliss, we raise our body's energetic vibration to a certain frequency, in which we are more capable of warding off pathogens and eliminating toxins from our system. Our thoughts can literally act like a shield. If, on the other hand, we feel anxious and dis-eased, we will quickly find that these thoughts become real in the body in the form of physical ailments."

"But how far can we go with this?" I interrupted. "I mean, if someone drinks poison, no matter how happy they are, they will surely die."

"Not necessarily. You must have heard the tales of the great shamans and yogis who perform physical feats that under normal circumstances would seem impossible. We are so much less limited than we are led to believe. We chip away at our limitations for lifetimes, but our mind keeps coming back to them, as if they gave us our identity, our sense of being. We need to remind ourselves that they are simply that: limitations, making us smaller than what we really are. How far can we go with this? As far as you want to take it, bearing in mind that the journey requires the right preparation of mind and body. You cannot ask a man who barely walks to run a marathon and expect he will complete it unharmed without any training.

"Now, even if your mother had been able to remain healthy against all odds and survive, it still wouldn't explain why she found herself in those circumstances in the first place. Why did they come to pollute her rivers and cut her forests? Was that also her manifestation? Did she subconsciously want to destroy all that she held dear? No, of course not. And that is where we move to another theme, more important than ever, which we haven't discussed yet: we are not alone on this planet. And we are affected by the thoughts of each and every one of its inhabitants."

As he spoke these words, I had a vision of the world from above. I saw millions of human beings like little ants crawling around. Each was shrouded in a cloud of pastel tones: the cloud of their beliefs, incessantly creating worlds around them. The mist spread from ant to ant, merging, colliding, strengthening common thoughts and dissipating secondary ones, until at a global scale it became a vast field of creation and destruction. Certain thoughts grew to enormous proportions, spurred on by the mental energy of countless humans. Others hung low on the horizon, shrinking slowly, eventually displaced by larger ones. It was fascinating and terrifying at once. I was witnessing our perpetual present crystalized out of the void of pure potential by the collective thoughts of humanity.

"And so unfortunately," he continued, "when enough people shift their attention away from nature and onto money, away from that which is life-giving and onto that which has become a palliative for their own need for approval, the world tips out of balance. So-called progress and growth, meaning the accumulation of even more money, become the priority, destroying everything else in their wake. Why? Because as you have seen, most of us suffer from the *not good enough* disease and believe that we are separate from each other and from the planet. As more and more minds hold these thoughts, they expand in the world, until they take on such tremendous proportions that nothing is good enough anymore. And we have forgotten what true connection is all about.

"Isolated and confused, in our disease, we grab onto anything that makes us feel better, seeking outside of ourselves that which can only be mended within. Regrettably, money and the material possessions that come with it have become the medicine of choice, the sought after Holy Grail, fleetingly giving people the illusion that they are worthy in their own eyes, that they are loved. It becomes a race without end, fuelled by our addictions, perpetuated by our collective delusion of separation.

"And thus, harmony and wellbeing become secondary. Our health fails, our families implode, we run around all day, like hamsters on our little wheels, returning home exhausted every evening, convincing ourselves that this is life. We may have started out well-intentioned and we may even feel that things are amiss, but we are trapped by the universal agreement, the voice of notoriety echoed by millions. We tell ourselves that we are sophisticated and smart and growing to our full potential, but the truth of the matter is: we are stuck in the status quo. We have surrendered our thinking to the collective agreement and are too scared to disagree, as this would trigger our deep-seated fear of rejection. Change has become undesirable.

"And so we comfort ourselves by planning our moments of pleasure and reward, where we get to spend the money we earned, spurred on by the voices around us fanatically encouraging us to consume, without a single thought towards Her, the source of our harmony. She who continues to give silently, without a word of complaint; She who is doing all she can to keep the world in balance when we, in our folly, endeavor to destroy Her day by day, chopping off the very arms holding us in their embrace.

"As you have realized in your own life, this is not sustainable, neither at the individual, nor at the global level. What you have experienced is nothing more than an exact mirror image of what is happening to the world. Through our bodies we are permanently connected with everything in the physical realm, in a very tangible way. Thus, when She suffers, we suffer. When She is out of balance, we are out of balance. In other words, when we take more than we give for decades on end, and She is no longer able to restore and replenish the abundance of life, the same holds true in our bodies. This is not conceptual. It is not a nice theory that we may think about in our moments of leisure. It is real. As are its consequences. And eventually, as you discovered personally, we collapse.

"What starts out as an isolated bout of pain, a valuable signal alerting us that we are out of balance, that something needs to be done, turns into chronic suffering because we choose to ignore it. Because it is easier to mask the pain, pretend it isn't there, and fail to notice that both our planet and our bodies are getting sicker and sicker. Whether we are aware of it or not, the global imbalance is affecting us all and has already taken many of us beyond a tipping point where our bodies have suddenly lost their tolerance for what we had unwisely considered 'normal'.

"In this game of mirrors, you will find that through your body, you echoed not only the turmoil of the planet, but also the life of your mother on a different scale. Your playground was not a small village in the rainforest, but the world. You didn't explicitly wish to die, but in a certain way, your thoughts and actions went against life. Your external poison was not only the oil – and its consequences at a global level – but the increasingly toxic world around you. A world where it had become impossible to breathe fresh air, drink pure water, eat food that does not contain harmful chemicals, and sleep deeply and peacefully unperturbed by damaging man-made waves. A world whose alarming external toxicity was compounded by the deleterious internal chemicals self-generated by the harmful thoughts you made your own."

As I listened to the Sage's words, I felt my life superimposing itself upon that of my mother, the two slowly melting into each other. I no longer knew who I was, what time period I was in, or even whether I was still alive. Suddenly, I saw the valley from above, as my mother had described it to me. And it was much worse than what she had seen. At the sight, my body started convulsing. There was no forest left around what had been my mother's village. Everything had been cut to the ground as far as the eye could see. The tree stumps dotting the landscape looked like the maimed limbs of gentle souls, slaughtered on the altar of man's confusion. My vision brought me closer and I saw that the village was deserted. The doors of some of the houses hanging desolately from their hinges. Not a bird singing. Not a child laughing. Only the reflection of the passing clouds on a dark murky puddle, and the sound of liquid dripping slowly from an abandoned pipe. Dripping, dripping incessantly, through the soil, into the ground water, until it reached the heart of the Mother, spread through her bloodstream, and poisoned her entire body.

I didn't want to continue witnessing this. It was too dark, too horrible. It felt too close. Everything became blurry. I thought I would faint. I heard a distant voice through my nausea, firm and clear. The Sage. "Keep looking," he insisted. "If you have the courage to keep looking, it will change."

I steadied myself upon the sound of these words and focused my entire attention on what I saw. He was right, it changed. But for the worse. I saw myself at a fork in the road. It was similar to the one in the Sage's story of the alcoholic contemplating the road leading to his death. But now, standing with me was all of humanity. Billions of men and women were huddled by my side, witnessing the futures that lay in potential in our collective mind. Straight before us lay a wide road. It was the road of my individual life. And it was also the road of our joint fate. It was a road lined with pipelines and growing cities spewing dark plumes of smoke into the air. It was a road of obscured skies, floods and storms. A road of pain and fear, power and domination. Cries of suffering rose from the ashen fields that we crossed, as we tripped over agonizing bodies and were hit by dead birds falling from the skies.

At the end of the road, there was a white sacrificial stone. And there sat the Pachamama, Gaia, our Mother Earth. Dressed in her last clothes of lush green forests and deep blue seas, fragrant flowers and flowing hair, a golden snake curled around her neck. She waited, looking at us with her eyes of bottomless compassion. The mass of humans formed a circle around her. And then, they pinned her down, raped her and slit her throat. Dark blood oozed out from all her pores, rapidly submerging us, drowning us mercilessly, down to the very last soul.

"No!" I cried. "No! That can't be! No!" My words were echoed by countless others. We pulled our hair and beat our chests, wailing helplessly as we contemplated the tragedy from above. And then, suddenly, we were all back at the fork in the road. And we saw a narrow trail winding its way up into the mountains. The air seemed pure up there, the forests green, and a crystalline stream flowed right down to our feet. In its sparkling swirls we read of a path of ease and flow, grace and joy, where life shone in the fullness of her glory.

Above the trail floated a sign, which read: "Oh fearless explorers about to tread upon this path, let it be known that these distant lands of which you have caught the scent and dreamed the bliss will only become real if you change your mind and cleanse yourself of your own confusion, discarding the centuries of waste you have accumulated. You must change your beliefs about yourself and the world, about what you value and what you will not tolerate. Life is to be reinstated at the core of your being. She is your first and only priority."

I blinked and opened my eyes. I was lying in Magdalena's arms, in the grass. I saw the clouds above me and felt the touch of the wind on my cheeks. I felt her warm hands holding mine, and in her eyes recognized the compassionate look I had seen on the Pachamama's face in my vision. I looked up at them, teary-eyed, barely coherent. And I mumbled, "And now what happens?"

"We change our minds, Maya." The Sage answered. I saw he was concerned. He had long seen the fork in the road and the paths that lay in waiting. "We change our minds," he repeated as if to himself.

"Remember," he added after a long silence, "that whatever we give our energy to expands in our lives. Just as the judgments and limited thinking we hold about ourselves and the world are leading to our annihilation, the opposite is also true. Everything radiates outwards from within. Each person who changes their mind transforms not only their lives, but also the world around them. And a mind that is cohesive, that knows without the shadow of a doubt that it is *good enough*, is ultimately more powerful and more creative than a fragmented mind. And therein lies our hope. Our creativity has the potential to overcome any obstacle, no matter how desperate the situation may seem. When we free our imagination from the heavy weights of our fear and confusion, a new path will naturally emerge.

"But it will not be easy. It will require us all to stop everything we are doing and have the courage to look at our addiction to our personal lies, how these have become our identity, how they have spread like a disease into the world. It will require us to look at what we value and how we lead our lives, what we say 'yes' to and what we say 'no' to. It will require us to understand that balance comes when our minds start to serve life as opposed to seeking to control her. And ultimately, as we undertake the journey of transformation, it will require us to become the ultimate observers of our minds and learn to value and hold a different state of being, a different energetic vibration.

"Only then will we heal ourselves, and by doing so, heal Her. Only then will we come into balance, and bring Her back into balance."

As I sat overlooking the lake, in the beautiful surroundings of this unique island, seemingly removed from what was occurring in other parts of the world, I wondered: How many of us, are prepared to take this narrow trail? How many are needed to change our collective fate?

XVI

Agape:
The Path of Unconditional Love

The Sage

I had left her before dawn, as had become our custom, knowing that with the first rays of the sun we both needed to tend to our respective duties: hers at the temple, mine in the village below the sanctuary. Yet that morning, I felt a gripping anxiety as I left. Something wasn't quite right, but I didn't know what it was. I didn't turn to go back and tell her about it. I didn't stop to reflect under the stars. Instead I walked on, driven by my habits, by the dictates of a mind that did not find any logical reason to worry and thus discredited the voice of warning which was wreaking havoc in my body.

I walked on. And those fatal seconds would change my entire life. And many lifetimes beyond that one. It is still a mystery to me how, in the space of one second, everything can change. One second she was there. And the next, she was gone. I spent years attempting to forgive myself for letting it happen, the heavy burden of guilt crushing my life. Now, I am an old man. So many have come to me for healing. As I watch them go with relief of body and mind, I sometimes wonder: am I healed yet? Or am I still carrying the bleeding wound of a broken heart? And I know that I owe it all to her: it is the soft pain throbbing in my heart that has enabled me to become a sought-after healer. By drinking at the source of my own suffering, I learned the true meaning of empathy, and later, of compassion.

On that morning, as I walked down towards the village in the dark, my distress only kept growing. Suddenly, I felt a presence behind me, shadows approaching fast. I started to run downhill, the sound of branches cracking under countless feet. How many could they be? I was unarmed, unprepared to confront them head-on. I ran straight towards the sheer cliffs that fell from the base of the village into the olive grove below. The first light of dawn miraculously came through as I reached the rocks, just in time to illumine the crack my body had steered me towards. It was a sort of chimney, in the fissures of which bushes had taken root, extending their branches towards me as a friend offering a hand. I did not hesitate. I jumped in, scrambling down a short distance, and then staying absolutely still. I heard the steps, along with a man's heavy breath passing by very close, running onwards along the edge of the cliffs. Others came behind and stopped. And then a voice, low and menacing, "Stick around! Make sure he doesn't come back alive."

Many thoughts crossed my mind as I huddled against the smooth rock with a thumping heart, waiting for the sounds of their steps to echo away, so that I could slide down unnoticed. I had made many enemies since we were sent on our journey to the Oracle, and I knew it. But I never thought that it would come to this. Not once did I think that they had been after the Priestess. Nor that her liaison with me had merely been a convenient reason to fire up passions and justify doing away with the woman who stood in the way of their full power. And in the process, they had found the perfect reason to eliminate me as well. The sun was rising, pulling me out of my reflections. I had to move fast. It would not take them long to follow the trail around the cliffs and spot me from the bottom.

I climbed down the rock face as quickly as I could and ran through the olive grove straight towards the sea. I wanted to go back up into the mountains, hide and somehow return to the sanctuary, find my way to her. But it was too risky as they could be coming down any side now. The only safe place I could think of was my ship, out on the blue waters that I loved. Whoever was after me would not follow me there. I ran straight towards the port without looking back, searching for my two trusted companions who had stayed behind to look after the boat. I found them sitting on the deserted shore. "We need to leave!" I uttered, breathless, both a plea and a command. "Now! As fast and as discretely as possible." They didn't ask any questions. The look on my face said it all and they were only too pleased to oblige. We jumped aboard and within minutes, the mooring was untied and we were gone.

The wind picked up, ballooning the sails and we made good progress through the sheltered cove. I sighed with relief and sat down on the deck, asking my companions to take over the tiller. My thoughts went to her. We were the only ship far and near and the color of our sails gave us away. Anyone could recognize us from the village, but not from the sanctuary, which lay out of sight. I connected with her in my heart, yearning for an opportunity to tell her all that was on my mind, vowing to come back to her. As I did, I felt a strange distress. Over the past months, I had felt her presence by my side even when she was not there physically. It was as if we had somehow merged at another level of existence, beyond space and time, where everything flowed in perfect harmony and words were superfluous. But something had changed and it made me increasingly anxious.

I was tempted to turn around. But I didn't think she was in danger, attributing my anxiety to the threats on my own life and concluding that a rash return would be unwise. A wave came crashing over board, instantly pulling me out of my hesitations into swift action to keep us on course and afloat. We had left the cove behind and entered into the open waters where the wind hit us with full force. After a few strenuous hours, burnt by the sun and the salt, exhausted from all that had come to pass that morning, I asked my companions to take over whilst I went to lie down in the cabin. No sooner had I closed my eyes and drifted into sleep, than she appeared before me.

She was beautiful in her white robes and long black hair, a soft light shining around her. But her eyes were sad as she lovingly looked into mine. "I had to go," she whispered with a desolate sigh. "I wish things had been different, but I had been warned before you came. As Her Oracle, I had proclaimed the beginning of a time of decline for the feminine force without and within. A time where Life would no longer be served, but increasingly controlled, her fierce beauty and untamed grace slowly extinguished. I never told you this, because you brought me such joy that I chose to ignore the prophecy that overshadowed your arrival. Little did I know that what She had called 'the end of an era' would be ushered in by my death."

She paused for a while, and then added, with a melancholic smile, "Do not mourn my death, for we are bonded beyond the confines of this life. It is good that you chose to live. A man like you is needed more than ever. Many will come to you for healing of body and mind, now and in many futures to come. And one day, what you have experienced in this lifetime will be played out on a grander scale, as all of humanity is invited to partake in the choice that will seal our collective fate as children of Gaia. Every thought will count more than ever before and the healing skills you will learn in this lifetime will become essential nourishment for countless parched souls, severed from the source, overwhelmed and lost in their own confusion." And then, she was gone.

I woke up devastated. I don't remember the rest of the journey. The pain was so intense that I became delirious. I just couldn't accept her death. I couldn't bear to think that I might have avoided it, had I stayed with her a little longer that morning, or turned back as my intuition had suggested. I understood that in her utter devotion to Gaia, she had been willing to sacrifice her human self for greater energies at play. I understood that we were connected in a realm beyond the physical and that a path had been laid in which I had a role to play. Yet the man I was cried the death of his beloved. I sat on the deck in sheer despair, holding on to the mast, eagerly waiting for the waves to crash over me and tear asunder the biting agony of loss. I must have looked miserable, the once-leader who used to be so calm and proud, drenched in sea-water and tears, screaming helplessly through the roaring waves and hurling winds.

My companions did not say a word. They steered our course magnificently through a raging sea. They took us home. As the first night fell, unable to unclasp me from the mast, let alone bring me to reason, they secured me to it with a rope, helped me drink some water, and left me there to purge my pain. I realized later how blessed I had been to have two such sailors with me, single-handedly navigating a ship that was designed for a crew of half a dozen, barely sleeping, while their captain sat incapacitated under the dark skies, feverishly battling his own demons. They told me later that seeing me in such a state scared them more deeply than any day at sea ever had. In the darkest hours of the night, they feared I might be possessed by a mythical demon that would bring doom to us all. Their senses sharpened by a keen determination to survive my madness, they took us to our homeland in a miraculous three days and three nights of stormy winds.

We were from the same village, a small fishing community

where life rolled peacefully through the rhythm of the seasons. I had not been back for what seemed an eternity. I don't remember our arrival. My companions carried me out of the boat and dragged me up into the little house where I had lived as a child. My younger sister was there, yet she did not recognize me. Not only had my features been distorted by the exhaustion and the pain, my face, beard and hair were completely covered in a white layer of crystalized salt. After the initial shock, she took care of me, patiently striving to bring me back to life.

But I was not ready to leave the land of the dead. Day and night I was tortured by the thought that I had been the one to bring about the end of an era. I had recurring dreams of a giant snake guarding the entrance to the sanctuary. The Priestess stood further up, looking down at me with sad knowing eyes. And I, sword in hand, desperately battled with the mythical son of Gaia, until I had slain its slithering form, only to realize with horror that I had killed my beloved and that everything around me had turned into an arid desert shimmering under the scorching sun.

I had sailed across the sea with harmony in my heart, intending to spread the healing light of the God of my forefathers. And yet, I had brought death and disharmony along with me. I had been blinded by an arrogant belief that I knew it all, that I held the keys of wisdom and truth in my hands. In my foolishness, I had not recognized the compassionate depth of those who had opened their hearts to my concealed conquering urges, those who knew all along what I had yet to discover through the burning fire of my pain.

Many weeks passed. Every day, my sister led me to the sea, where she sat me on a rock and left me in the affectionate company of my faithful old dog. She hoped that the sight that had stirred my passions as a young boy would once again work its miracles and reignite my desire for life. Sometimes one of my companions or an acquaintance from the village would visit me, curious to see what I had become. The rumors had spread fast about my desolate state, yet no one knew what had happened. Imaginations flourished filling in the details with countless stories, from the most extravagant and magical to the mundane and grotesque. None of it mattered to me. I did not care for human company and had not uttered a single word since my arrival. The villagers' initial curiosity and appetite for intrigue eventually waned and I was left alone with my empathic dog and the loving care of my sister.

One day, as I sat there, something caught my attention. By my feet lay a freshly shed snake skin. It was in one piece, beautiful and delicate. I picked it up and stared at it for a long time. It was as if nature had offered me an insight to my own healing. As I held the old discarded skin in my hands, running my fingers over its fine transparent scales, I understood that I was ready to start forgiving myself for what had come to pass. It was time for me to shed my pain and slip out into a new phase, a new possibility for growth. I breathed in the fresh salty air and became aware of the strength in my body. I looked at the red earth and the rocks, the seagulls crying out over the water and the distant horizon. My dog jumped to his feet and started barking at me. Yes, I was back. I once again felt the call of life pulsating through my veins.

My sister was overjoyed when she saw me coming back to the house that afternoon. "I thought we had lost you," she said. "Your eyes. You were so far away." I was filled with gratitude for her love and the attention of those who had not given up on me, who had simply been there, patiently looking after me with the absolute faith that I would eventually build the strength needed for my own healing.

From then on, I fully integrated the community life, pleased to be of service and focus on strenuous physical chores that took my mind away from the pain that sometimes still welled up from within. The sea lured me to its magical blue waters, but in its breeze I tasted the salty memory of a man lashed to a mast, drowning in his tears as he held on to the lifeless body of his beloved. I was still vulnerable and knew I had to stay away. I renounced fishing in favor of other tasks, maintaining the boats, repairing the houses and tilling the fields. It was a new life for me, because I had left the village many years before as a young man. I had worked under my father who was a healer officiating on behalf of the great God curing the illnesses of body and mind. I had spent years learning from him, faithfully assisting him in the sanctuary up in the green hills.

One day, I had heard of the fame of the Oracle of distant lands, the beautiful Priestess of flowing black hair who saw through the hearts of men and spoke on behalf of the mystical Goddess of times past, the Great Mother of Life. Instantly, her image had engraved itself on my heart, along with an aching desire to go find her. The mere thought of her melted my heart, as if we had always known each other, as if our coming together was as inevitable as the soft glow of the moon on a cloudless night. And thus it had come to be. I was born at a time when temples to honor our God were being built all over the land, and I had promptly volunteered for the mission to bring His shining light to the land of the Oracle. I had left in pure devotion, but as I fatefully came to experience, the men who had accompanied me harbored desires of power that ultimately crushed not only the woman I loved, but also the divine One she had come to embody.

The hard work in the village helped steer my mind away from such painful memories, keeping me immersed in a time before the Oracle, a time of innocence, free from the greed and lust of men, free from the pullulating sickness of fragmented minds. I focused all my efforts on living in the present, as if my past had ceased to exist and my future was irrelevant, silencing the memory of the mysterious prophecy the Priestess had left me with.

But one evening, my father appeared at the door. His wise eyes took me in earnestly, intensely scanning through all the layers of my being, as if he could see it all, understand it all. He took my arms and simply said, "We need you at the sanctuary. Please come back with me." And in that moment, I heard her whispering in my ear, "Many will come to you for healing of body and mind, now and in many futures to come…" And so, the next day, I followed my father back to the hills, ready to become the healer I had somehow chosen to be.

It was a beautiful place, set in a forested valley of pines and springs. The air had a vivifying quality, which alone helped ease the burden of those who made it to our sacred grounds. I had only been gone a few years, yet much had changed in my absence. The stone building that welcomed and housed the afflicted had been expanded, along with the space for ritual meals in honor of the God that preceded the deeper healing work, which we performed in the temple by the sacred well. No wonder my father had come to get me: people were flocking to our sanctuary, which I interpreted as yet another sign of the beginning of the time of decline.

The first woman I was to take care of bore an eerie resemblance to the Priestess. I hesitated when my father brought her to me, my throat closing from a sudden pang of pain, but he spurred me on, giving me the courage to look her in the eyes and open my heart to assist in her healing, which I later understood was also to be mine. Her story was a tragic story of loss. She had lost her two small children and was tormented by a strange disease that had paralyzed one side of her body. She walked with a stick and had dragged herself up from the sea, through the hills all the way to the sanctuary on her own, with a determination that made me pale before my own fragility in the face of loss.

The death of her children had been an accident, yet she blamed herself for it. Her despair was so severe and her guilt so paralyzing that it literally settled in her body, immobilizing her limbs almost completely. After extensive preparatory rituals and purifications, I led her into the temple and accompanied her on a dream-journey into her mind, where the healing God appeared, whispering of forgiveness. He asked that she let go of the feelings of resentment and hatred she harbored towards herself because she believed she should have prevented the death of the beings she loved so deeply. He asked that she embrace herself fully and release the physical punishment she was ruthlessly inflicting upon herself with her own mind. Within a week of working together, she walked out of the valley without a stick, with a timid smile on her lips and hope in her heart.

It was my journey as much as it was hers. My feelings of guilt were still coming up for air every now and then, playing out in my dreams. One morning, with the coming of spring, as I was waking, I saw the image of the young girl that the Priestess had trained to become the next Oracle. I worried about her wellbeing. She was a shining light, a budding force of nature able to channel the formidable power of Gaia. Yet, she was young and vulnerable and the priests who had planned my assassination would surely spare no effort to intimidate her and bring her under their dominion. I feared that she might become another victim of my recklessness. I sent for my trusted companions in the village and asked them to bring her a coded message of invitation, upon her first appearance as the Oracle. I wanted to protect her, to do for her what I had been unable to do for the woman I loved.

But she didn't come. She sent me a response that made my whole body shiver, "She, in inner form has come to him. She, in outer form, need not come," the Oracle had said. Was it really true? Had I genuinely reconnected to the archaic forces of the Great Mother? Had I been able to resuscitate from within that which I had been instrumental in destroying without?

I thought about my patients and the many women who came

to me for healing of body and mind. And I understood that through them, I was able to touch the indomitable strength of Woman, her power and her passion, her capacity to survive and rekindle her love when all around her has been broken. It was as if Gaia herself lived on in the bodies of all these women who carried the fire of Life in their womb, eager to live and love, learn and die, fall and stand back up, time after time. Through their eyes, I was able to peer through the ages, unlocking the great mysteries of time. And I saw that Her spirit could never be vanquished. No matter how hard we tried to squash her, Life would always rise up again and give us another chance to reconnect to the source, to come into wholeness. Yet, I was also shown that many paths were possible and the form in which we chose to partake in our own evolution lay entirely in our hands.

XVII

Apotheosis:
The Priestess Reborn

Maya

The skies were dark when I awoke the following morning. A storm was brewing over the island. As I set my bare feet onto the earthen floor of my cave, everything felt different. I was no longer agitated nor distressed. I felt calm, with a newfound clarity of purpose and a powerful sense of resolve. I peeked out of the crack in the rock at the first drops of rain and saw Saywa – for now I knew her by her true name – swiftly walking down to get me. Through gusts of wind, she led me back to the big cave. The Sage was waiting for us at the entrance, torches in hand.

The thunder echoed against the cliffs as we jumped into the long narrow corridor that entered deep into the mountain, leaving behind the fresh smell of the pouring rain. Guided by the light of the torches, we crossed the first cave until we reached the stream rushing out of the rock at the back. There, we entered another passageway that twisted and turned, eventually opening up into a second cave of gigantic proportions. From where we stood, we could not see how far it went. I just noticed that the ground sloped downward ever so slightly, and after a few more steps, I started to make out the lake, its transparent waters mysteriously shining in the dark.

And then, I knew. This was the heart. The meandering journey I had travelled in my mind had found its resonance in the physical plane. I had made it to the heart of the labyrinth! I stood in awe before the dark waters. Black as the night, still as the void, they whispered of the primordial longing that gave rise to creation. I witnessed nothingness molded into being by the creative power of the mind, only to be engulfed again into the bottomless womb of Gaia in a cyclical spiral of creation and destruction. I saw the images from my first vision in trance, shimmering on the surface of the waters. Once again, I was gazing into a dark mirror at the reflection of my own soul, and heard Her voice, *"You are Energy refining itself. You are Love experiencing itself. You are Life becoming more."* I dissolved into Her. I became all of creation. I became the bottomless void. I became the primordial womb at the source of Life.

Whilst I remained transfixed by the Mystery, Saywa and the Sage built a fire on the shore next to me. They sat down and gently called my name. Maya. By naming who I was, they called me back into beingness, rebirthing me into my body. I turned and smiled, ecstatic before the beauty of my rebirth to myself, and joined them around the fire, relishing the sound of crackling flames and their golden reflection on the dark still waters.

Words had become superfluous. We were absorbed in the intensity of all that had come to pass since I had set foot on this island and the simple joy of being alive and feeling connected so deeply to one another. What had started as an exploration into my mind, a way for me to find healing, had become so much more. Together, we had journeyed down the road of human potential and witnessed its daunting pitfalls and dazzling opportunities. And from the collective, we had come back again to the individual, the only place there ultimately was, the only place change could happen.

After a while, Saywa turned to me and gently said, "It has been a long and challenging, amazing and beautiful journey for all of us. Over this past week, thanks to you, we too have passed through countless doors and tied loose threads. To close the circle, I would like us to express our gratitude for the guidance that brought us back together, and invite you to join me in a dance of completion. A dance to thank each other and honor our Mother Earth, Her inexhaustible capacity to love and bring forth everlasting life."

The Sage pulled a drum out, seemingly from nowhere, and started to beat a slow steady rhythm that instantly got me to my feet. The sound of the drum awakened an archaic urge in my body to connect with the timeless and formless that exists in the continuity of movement throughout the ages. My body began to move of its own accord, twisting and turning, rolling and flowing. As the beat gradually rose, I followed, whirling faster and faster, at one with life, joining earth and sky with my bare feet and open palms. My eyes were almost closed and I only remember glimpses of rock, flames and water, the Sage, the fire and Saywa, spinning past, melting into each other.

I journeyed through worlds of rhythm and silence, light and shadow, until the beat slowed down and so did I, coming back to the reality of where I was. Slowly, I opened my eyes, stunned to find that I was on my own. The fire was still burning and three torches were set in the ground, encircling the space I had been dancing in. But otherwise, there was no sign of another human presence in the cave. I shuddered and sat down, catching my breath, trying to understand what was going on. Where had they gone? Why didn't they say anything? How had I not noticed them leaving?

I had seen so many visions over the past week, countless

journeys into other people's minds and into my own. I had broken through so many boundaries between the seen and the unseen, the past and the future, the real and the imaginary. I had seemingly fulfilled the shaman's prophecy to my mother of my capacity to see and bridge worlds. Could it be that I had lost myself in the process, that I no longer was able to distinguish a vision from reality, a dream from a waking state? Had these wonderful beings really been of flesh and bone, or had they merely been projections of my mind?

Utterly confused, I recalled everything I had learned over the past week, searching desperately for answers. And suddenly, a sparkle caught my eye. On the floor by the black waters, lay Saywa's silver brooch: a sign that they had been here after all. I picked it up and saw that it represented a snake curled up in a spiral, a promise of healing, of the cyclical shedding of the old to embrace the new, of transmutation to another state of consciousness.

As I admired its silvery shine and attempted to pierce its secrets, I heard her voice. It was Saywa, my teacher and guide. And at the same time, it was Gaia, the source I had learned to connect with many eons ago, as if their voices had merged into one. "Maya," she said, "It was time for us to ride through the rhythm of the fire and go back to the formless where we belong. Even though it may seem that we have parted, we are still with you. In fact, we are you. We are the infinite within you, the part of your body and mind that knows and guides you every moment. You can access us at any time, simply by being, simply by paying attention."

I sat by the fire, listening to these words, but could still not understand. It didn't make any sense. I was overcome by a great sadness. How could this happen yet again? I had found the beings I loved most, only to have them disappear so soon, leaving me confused and on the verge of insanity. Was this what it meant to break through all limitations, including the mirage of separation? It was deeply painful and utterly challenging. The human side of me cried their physical disappearance in sheer disbelief, while my higher self blissfully smiled, knowing that pain and attachment were not necessary, for indeed, they were alive within me, whispering their wisdom through the silence.

Lost in the duality of this experience, at once human and divine, I slowly found my way back to the first cave that had offered me its secrets. I stopped before the narrow corridor leading out into the world. And as I stared at the smooth stone archway, it dawned on me that this was the meandering path out from the labyrinth, replete with obscure distractions and tempting junctions that would invite me astray. I could see a faint light in the distance, a promise of a different future, a different potentiality for my own life and for the Earth. And I knew that I was ready.

I had learned that I manifest my own reality, that my mind is a constellation of intricate beliefs continuously creating my life from the void of pure potential. I had looked dispassionately at my subconscious beliefs, my patterns and wounds stretching back over centuries, how these had formed, and how the fear of rejection and my addiction to others' approval had kept me stuck in a cycle of self-destruction.

I had understood that all of this was a result of my confusion about the true nature of my being. I had pierced the illusion of separation and reconnected to Her, to the Life stirring within and without, the divine feminine, my Mother and body, my blood and soul. I had found my way back to the One who pulsates at the core of my being, flooding me with Love and pure creativity, the One to whom I would henceforth dedicate every breath of my life.

And from there, I had started to rewrite the script of my life, saturating my mind with the circumstances I henceforth wanted to attract. I knew that on the long journey back out, I needed to immerse myself in a supportive environment, and become the ultimate observer of my mind, acutely vigilant of any remaining limiting beliefs or engrained patterns attempting to sabotage my creations. I needed to slow down, aware of what I said yes to, and what I said no to, so as to direct my energy exclusively towards that which was aligned with my true essence and purpose.

And I had another powerful tool at my disposal: I had reconnected to my body and understood how to listen to its wisdom, knowing that its profound guidance would take me closer and closer to whatever made me feel healthy and relaxed, vibrant and strong, away from the pressure of needing to be perfect and into the unpredictable yet always generous flow of life.

Yes, I was ready. Taking a deep breath, I slid out of the belly of the mountain, into bright sunshine, and blinked in awe at the glistening hills cleansed by the rains. I sat down at the mouth of the cave, contemplating the beautiful land touching the heavens that had witnessed my transformation. And I prayed that enough of us would have the strength to heal ourselves, and that in doing so, we would succeed in bringing Her back into balance.

They say that she who has rested in the heart of the Great Labyrinth is forever changed, henceforth walking in the footsteps of the great Priestesses of times long past. They say that she who has courageously followed the tortuous path into the darkest corners of her mind, and found her way out by the light of her inner clarity, brings back the map to the journey of transformation.

And on this complex pathway towards exclusivity of thinking, they say that when we find ourselves clinging to the illusion of separation, indulging in the fleeting yet tenacious belief that we are *not good enough*, we may call on Her to compassionately hold us as we cry. She is there to remind us of the perfection of our human imperfection in this dynamic dance called Life, until we become aware of Her grander presence and feel the arms of Gaia holding us in the ultimate embrace of unconditional Love.

And when we doubt the power of our mind, She is there to show us what is at stake, and what is possible. To remind us that we are the masters of our reality. That whatever we focus our thoughts, our words, our feelings and our actions on, we bring into form. That we have the capacity to manifest a beautiful vision of life on Earth, of harmony restored, if we change the field of our collective beliefs and steer our course along the narrow trail leading up into the pure hills.

They say the time may come when Gaia will rise from the sacrificial stone borne of our pain and our confusion, walk towards us and take our hands as we consciously choose a different future.

And all it will take, is for us to change the beliefs we hold.

About who and what we really are.

They say that it can happen at any time.

It could happen now.

Are you ready?

Galaxidi, Greece, June 21st 2014

The night of the Willakuti